A GUIDE TO

ANGELFISHES &
BUTTERFLYFISHES

Gerald R. Allen   Roger Steene   Mark Allen

TROPICAL REEF RESEARCH

ODYSSEY
PUBLISHING

Acknowledgements

This book would not have been possible without the cooperation of the following colleagues who generously donated photographs: Dieter Eichler (Germany); Kiyoshi Endoh (Tokyo, Japan); Helmut Debelius (Ikan Unterwasserarchiv, Frankfurt Germany); Bob Halstead (Cairns, Australia); Dr. Phil Heemstra (J.L.B. Smith Institute of Ichthyology, Grahamstown, South Africa); Tomonori Hirata (Tokyo, Japan); Rudie H. Kuiter (Aquatic Photographics, Seaford, Victoria, Australia); Randall Kosaki (Ikan); Michael Moxter (Mühlheim, Germany); Robert Myers (Coral Graphics, Guam); Yohji Ohkata (Tokyo, Japan); Peter Parker (Broken Head, New South Wales, Australia); Richard Pyle (Bishop Museum, Honolulu); Dr. John E. Randall (Bishop Museum, Honolulu); Ed Robinson (Ikan/Hawaiian Water Colors, Maui, Hawaii); H. Voigtmann (Ikan); and, P. Woodhead (Ikan).

Richard Pyle not only allowed us to use his excellent photographs, but also supplied information regarding the scientific classificaiton of these fishes. He also gave us detailed information about his exploration of the deep reef habitat.

Jill Ruse (Perth, Australia) prepared paintings of *Prognathodes guyotensis* and *Chaetodontoplus niger*. The illustration of the juvenile stages of *Apolemichthys kingi* was painted by Elaine Heemstra. Hiroyuki Tanaka (Tokyo, Japan) helped us to arrange the use of photographs by Japanese photographers. Lyle Squire Jr. (Cairns Marine Aquarium Fish) supplied ecological information pertaining to West African species.

Professor Bruno Condé (University of Nancy, France) kindly supplied us with longevity data for angelfishes and butterflyfishes living in the Nancy Aquarium.

Finally, we thank Connie Allen for preparing the bibliography.

ISBN: 0-9661720-1-9

Design and layout: Mark Allen
Cover design: Robyn Mundy
Maps and line drawings: Mark Allen
Manuscript prepared by Gerald R. Allen and Mark Allen

Colour separations by Exposure Graphics, East Perth WA
Printed by Vanguard Press, Perth WA 6003

Published by Odyssey Publishing/Tropical Reef Research
Distributed by Odyssey Publishing (USA)/Tropical Reef Research (Aust.)

Cover photos: Peppermint Angelfish, *Paracentropyge boylei* (photo by Richard Pyle) and Spot-Tail Butterflyfish, *Chaetodon ocellicaudus* (photo by Roger Steene).

CONTENTS

INTRODUCTION

Angelfishes and butterflyfishes are among nature's most beautiful creatures. Their popularity as aquarium fishes is perhaps surpassed only by clownfishes (*Amphiprion*). No public aquarium would be complete without at least one display showcasing their beauty and grace. Thanks to a dazzling array of color patterns they are keenly sought by underwater photographers. Diving enthusiasts, beginners and veterans alike, appreciate their distinct, emblazoned patterns. Although a host of species are involved, 83 angelfishes and 121 butterflyfishes to be exact, these two groups are among the easiest of reef fish to identify. Their ready identification coupled with a strong affinity for coral-rich environments makes them ideal "indicators" of coral reef biodiversity. An argument can definitely be advanced for the premise that areas rich in butterflys and angels will also exhibit an abundance of coral species and a wealth of other marine life forms.

Although most angelfishes and butterflyfishes live on tropical coral reefs, these groups are also present on rocky reefs in subtropical and warm seas such as those found along the coast of Japan, South Africa, southern Australia, and even occasionally off southern California. Two genera of butterflyfish: *Chelmonops* (with two southern Australian species), and; *Amphichaetodon* (with a pair of southern Pacific species), are exclusively restricted to cooler seas. Shallow sunlit reefs are the principle domain of both families. The majority of species occur in less than 20 m depth, well within reach of SCUBA divers. In fact, many can be viewed by snorkeling in places such as Australia's Great Barrier Reef.

Despite their popularity, no previous book has provided complete coverage of both closely related families. The most comprehensive publication to date was a two-volume work, *Butterfly and Angelfishes of the World* (Mergus Publishers). Volume one (1978) by Roger Steene covered all the species found in the Australia-New Guinea region. The second volume (1979) by Gerald Allen included the remaining species of the world. Although all the known species were treated in these volumes, the unorthodox scope of coverage in each prevents them as serving as a practical reference. Therefore, we decided to consolidate our knowledge of these popular fishes by producing the first-ever guide specially designed to satisfy the needs of both divers and aquarists. Moreover, in the intervening years since the Mergus volumes were published, a number of new species have been discovered, and a wealth of new photographic material is now available.

How to use this book

The book is designed as an identification and reference guide. Preliminary chapters (1 and 2) provide basic information on angelfishes and butterflyfishes, including sections dealing with morphology, distribution, classification, and life history. The individual species accounts comprise the "heart" of the book. Each species occupies a full page and features an illustration of the adult and juvenile (only if colors are sufficiently different) and a distribution map. The text is divided into brief sections covering habitat, useful features (usually color) for identification, remarks about behavior and general biology, and geographic distribution. In order to facilitate its use as an efficient field guide we have divided the species accounts into two sections, corresponding with two major geographic regions: Indo-west and central Pacific (Chapter 3), and the eastern Pacific and Atlantic (Chapter 4).

There is no doubt that color patterns of angelfishes and butterflyfishes are their most distinctive trait. Therefore, the book is designed to take maximum advantage of this feature. The user is advised to simply flip through the pages, noting the patterns of the various species, when using the volume for identification purposes. In order to make the book even more "user friendly" we have departed from the traditional alphabetical presentation of species. Instead, species which display similar patterns are grouped together. **The most closely related species, often displaying remarkably similar color patterns, are placed opposite each other for ready comparison.**

Opposite: Typical angelfish and butterflyfish habitat at Kimbe Bay on the island of New Britain, Papua New Guinea (Photo by Gerald R. Allen).

Detailed advice on the successful maintenance of angelfishes and butterflyfishes in the aquarium is presented in Chapter 5. In addition, this icon appears in the species sections for those fishes that are presently available in the aquarium trade and are deemed suitable for captivity. See page 232 for an explanation of the star system.

A list of references is given at the end of the book. There is a large body of literature available on butterflyfishes and angelfishes. Most of these are technical scientific reports or popular books dealing with all the fishes of a particular region. We have only selected references that we feel will prove the most useful for anyone seeking additional information about these fishes.

A summary of the classification of angelfishes and butterflyishes is presented in separate appendices at the end of the book. This includes a capsule summary of the important characters for distinguishing genera and subgenera, as well as a complete listing of species contained in the various subgroups.

Endangered species

The World Conservation Union (IUCN) periodically publishes its Red List of Threatened Animals: an exhaustive catalogue which categorizes endangered species or ones that are potentially threatened. IUCN relies on the advice of scientific researchers in assigning species to one of the eight following categories: extinct; extinct in the wild; critically endangered; endangered; vulnerable; lower risk; data deficient, and; not evaluated. The list traditionally included mainly higher vertebrates such as birds and mammals, but in the past decade an effort has been made to expand coverage to all groups, including fishes. Freshwater ecosystems are particularly vulnerable to the onslaught of civilization, hence there is an urgent need to implement conservation measures at many locations in order to conserve disappearing populations of native fishes. For this reason the latest (1996) Red List contains hundreds of freshwater fishes. On the contrary, few marine fishes are listed as the population status is generally much more difficult to assess. Generally marine populations are less vulnerable, although exceptions include certain food fishes and coral reef species of Southeast Asia, which are highly vulnerable due to habitat destruction by illegal fishing methods (explosives, cyanide, etc.).

Angelfish and butterflyfish populations appear to be in excellent shape as far as their conservation status is concerned, although six species appear in the 1996 Red List (listed below). All six species are assigned under the vulnerable category, mainly because most are restricted to tiny island localities and therefore have a very limited population size.

- Resplendent Pygmy Angelfish (*Centropyge resplendens*) - Ascension Island
- Yellow-crowned Butterflyfish (*Chaetodon flavocoronatus*) - Guam
- South African Butterflyfish (*Chaetodon marleyi*) - South Africa
- Oblique Butterflyfish (*Chaetodon obliquus*) - St. Paul's Rocks (mid-Atlantic)
- Easter Island Butterflyfish (*Chaetodon litus*) - Easter Island
- Robust Butterflyfish (*Chaetodon robustus*) - West Africa

Historical background

Carole Linnaeus, the Swedish botanist and father of our modern system of binomial nomenclature began the quest for discovering new species of angelfishes and butterflyfishes. The following eight species were described and given their Latin names in the first edition of his "Systema Naturae" in 1758: *Chaetodon capistratus, C. striatus, C. vagabundus, Chelmon rostratus, Holacanthus ciliaris,* and *Pomacanthus arcuatus.* Linnaeus's concept of classification was based on only a fraction of the living organisms we now recognize, hence it suffered from oversimplification. For example, he placed all eight of the species listed above in the genus *Chaetodon*, which he described in this same publication.

The period spanning the next hundred years, or approximately between 1760-1860, was truly the golden age of natural history exploration. About one half of the presently known species in these two families were collected and described during this period. Scientists and naturalists from a host of nations, particularly England, Holland, France, and Germany, were invariably present on voyages of exploration to the far corners of the globe. Consequently, new species were discovered at a relatively rapid rate. Two scientists who were particularly prolific in terms of describing new species were Baron Georges Cuvier, who worked in the Natural History Museum in Paris, and Pieter Bleeker, the famous Dutch Ichthyologist. Cuvier attempted to review all the known species of butterflyfishes and angelfishes in Volume 7 of the monumental *Histoire Naturelle des Poissons* (co-authored with Achille Valenciennes), published in 1831. Twenty-five species (19 butterflys and 6 angels), currently recognized as valid were originally described and given their scientific names in this publication.

Pieter Bleeker described five species each of angelfishes and butterflyfishes that are still regarded as valid. Although this contribution may not seem particularly noteworthy, the importance of his voluminous ichthyological works in providing a solid foundation for our knowledge of Indo-Pacific fishes cannot be understated. Considering that he was employed as a Dutch Army surgeon during his tenure in Indonesia (1842-1860), the extent of his ichthyological activity was remarkable. During a research career that spanned 36 years Bleeker published 500 papers that include descriptions of an incredible number of new taxa: 406 genera and 3,324 species. Approximately 75 percent of these published articles were devoted to the Indonesian fauna. Bleeker's knowledge of Indonesian fishes, both freshwater and marine, was outstanding. Revisions of various groups of Indo-Pacific fishes by modern researchers frequently attest to Bleeker's uncanny intuition and astute understanding of natural relationships. His work on East Indian angelfishes and butterflyfishes culminated in Volume 9 of his celebrated ichthyological "Atlas" published in 1877.

The number of new species gradually diminished over the next century, creating a false impression that, perhaps due to their conspicuous patterns and habits, all of the world's angelfishes and butterflyfishes had been documented. Nothing could be further from the truth. The late Jaques Cousteau's development of SCUBA as a scientific research tool has had a profound impact on ichthyological exploration for the past half-century. The use of SCUBA has pioneered a new era of exploration. The discovery of at least eight new butterflyfishes and 22 angelfishes over the past few decades can be directly linked to the use of this equipment. Moreover, SCUBA has allowed divers and amateur naturalists free access to the secret undersea world of these beautiful fishes, resulting in valuable information about their behavior and other aspects of the life history.

Exploring the "Twilight Zone"

If you are impressed with the Peppermint Angelfish that adorns the cover of this book you are not alone. That's why we selected it. We could scarcely believe our eyes when a photo of this gorgeous fish first appeared in a Japanese magazine several years ago. No doubt existed about it being a new species. It was certainly not an angelfish we were familiar with. Unfortunately the text was in Japanese, which left us puzzled about its origins. We should have realized at once that Rich Pyle was involved in its discovery and subsequent collection. This man's obsession with deep-diving is matched only by his passion for discovering new fishes that inhabit what he calls the "twilight zone". This is the unexplored portion of the world's coral reefs lying at depths between 60-150 meters, immediately below the safe limit for SCUBA diving, and above the poorly lit edge of the abyss, where life-sustaining photosynthesis ceases. This lower extension of the reef habitat is home to numerous fishes and other animals, yet to be discovered by scientists.

Rich currently works in the Ichthyology Department of the Bishop Museum and is pursuing a Ph.D. degree at the University of Hawaii. The subject of his thesis study is the classification of angelfishes. At the age of 19 he suffered a near fatal attack of decompression sickness ("bends"), as a result of surfacing too quickly from a deep dive at Palau. He was initially paralyzed from the neck down, but fortunately made a full recovery after a year-long convalescence. Badly shaken by this experience,

Rich resolved to continue diving but set about designing a safer system for deep-water exploration. Initially he settled on a SCUBA unit that utilized mixed gases, thus avoiding the debilitating effect of nitrogen when breathed at great depths. However, there were still major problems: the allowable time on the bottom was far too brief for serious exploration, and; the depths involved called for exceedingly long and boring decompression stops on the way back to the surface.

That's why he eventually switched to a rebreather (a closed circuit SCUBA system) in which expelled air is breathed over and over. This sort of system relies on the removal of dangerous carbon dioxide by means of a mechanical "scrubber". The rebreather allows lengthy bottom times and greatly reduces the duration of decompression stops. The only trouble is the gear is very sophisticated, requiring a long-training period and intimate knowledge of its mechanical and electronic details. Also, it's very expensive - the Cis-Lunar rebreather Pyle currently uses is worth US $50,000! This is far beyond the means of a struggling graduate student, but fortunately he has been able to attract sponsorship from both the dive industry and the media.

Underwater explorer Richard Pyle prepares for a dive into the "twilight zone" with his revolutionary rebreather apparatus.

H. Gert DeCouet

Getting back to the story of the mysterious angelfish - it was first seen in October 1989 by aquarium fish collector Charles Boyle using conventional SCUBA gear at a depth of 93 meters at Rarotonga in the Cook Islands. He wrote to Rich Pyle about his observations and exactly two months later this intrepid pair made several dives at Rarotonga to depths between 90-112 meters. They succeeded in capturing three specimens of the "peppermint" angel, as well as two additional individuals of another new, bright yellow *Centropyge*. The initial dives were made with normal SCUBA gear, as this was just prior to Rich's experimentation with mixed gases. We definitely <u>do not</u> recommend using conventional SCUBA for these sort of depths, unless you have a death wish! The effect of nitrogen "narcosis" at a depth of 300 feet is equivalent to that of drinking six martinis - it's hard to stay awake let alone concentrate on fish collecting.

Recently, we asked Richard to recount his first encounter with the new angels at Rarotonga. He replied, "There's not much to tell. The truth is, I suffered so badly from narcosis I couldn't remember collecting the fish after surfacing. I actually thought we had failed, and was astonished, not to mention embarrassed, when it was pointed out to me that I had the fish in my collecting bag." The new *Centropyge* was eventually named *C. narcosis*, certainly a fitting appellation. Two years later Pyle returned to Rarotonga to collect additional specimens of the two angelfishes. This time he and Boyle employed mixed gases, a much safer proposition, but still not without hazards. Incidentally, Pyle financed the cost of his trip to Rarotonga by selling some of the live angelfish specimens to an aquarium fish wholesaler for the princely sum of US $600 each. He felt real good about this transaction until hearing the Peppermint Angel eventually retailed in Japan for 1.4 million yen each or about $14,000!

Richard Pyle observes *Chaetodon tinkeri* on a deep reef in Hawaii's "twilight zone". The curious onlooker is a gray reef shark (*Carcharhinus amblyrhynchos*).

Angelfish treasures from the "twilight zone". These are the deepest dwelling members of the angelfish family currently known to science, *Paracentropyge boylei* (left), and *Centropyge narcosis* (right).

The "twilight zone" holds real promise for future new discoveries. It is probably safe to say that any angelfishes or butterflyfishes still undetected are living in this zone. Rich admits he has barely scratched the surface. Other than numerous test dives at his home base in Hawaii he has only utilized the new Cis-Lunar rebreather on a couple of expeditions to Palau and Papua New Guinea. On the latter trip he discovered over 30 new species (no butterfly or angelfishes). This is certainly the beginning of an exciting new era of coral reef exploration, one that's sure to include the discovery of rare and beautiful angelfishes and butterflyfishes.

CHAPTER 1

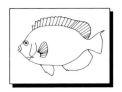

INTRODUCING ANGELFISHES

Angelfishes are understandably a special favorite of divers and aquarists. There are few sights underwater more impressive than the majestic appearance of a large *Pomacanthus* or *Holacanthus* angel. They are relatively uncommon, and invariably make an impression no matter how many times they are seen. Renowned German photojournalist and good friend Helmut Debelius was so smitten with his first encounters with the lovely Blue-ringed Angelfish (*Pomacanthus annularis*) that he has adopted this fish as his personal logo. He has gone so far as to have one entire side of his three-story home in suburban Frankfurt decorated with a massive portrait of this species. We don't expect everyone to be moved to this extent, but we guarantee the first impression of these gorgeous fishes will be a lasting one. Young angelfishes, with their stunning "billboard" color patterns, have long been a premier attraction in the aquarium hobby. The fascinating changes in color pattern which typifies the genera *Pomacanthus* and *Holacanthus* offer an added bonus for angelfish aficionados.

Morphology

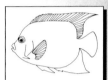

Angelfishes have been traditionally lumped with butterflyfishes based on their similar anatomy. However, all recent authors have separated them, based on sound internal and external morphological differences. Although angelfishes are generally more robust and more uniformly ovate-shaped, the most obvious feature distinguishing them from butterflyfishes is the prominent spine on the rear corner of the cheek (see photo below), which is always absent in butterflyfishes. Angelfishes are further characterized by a combination of features that include the absence of a scaly process at the base of the pelvic fins, rougher scale margins (due to presence of small spines or ctenii), distinct ridges on the exposed portions of the scales, and a postlarval stages lacking the elaborate plates and head spines that typify the *tholichthys* stage of butterflyfishes.

Roger Steene

Angelfishes are characterised by a prominent spine on the lower edge of the cheek. This feature is clearly visible on this individual of *Chaetodontoplus conspicillatus*.

Opposite: *Centropyge interrupta* (female) from Midway Islands, Hawaii (Photo by Richard Pyle).

Distribution

Angelfishes occur throughout tropical and subtropical latitudes and are most often associated with coral reefs. The majority of species inhabit the vast ocean, commonly referred to as the Indo-Pacific, stretching from the shores of East Africa to the Americas. All but 13 Atlantic and eastern Pacific species, approximately 89 percent of all species, inhabit the Indo-Pacific. Australia with 24 species represented, has more angelfishes than any other country in the world.

Within the Indo-Pacific region each species is variably distributed. Six have very broad distributions ranging across the Indian Ocean and enveloping most of the western part of the Pacific. Twelve have ranges covering various parts of the Indian Ocean, including the Red Sea. The remaining species inhabit various parts of the central and western Pacific, including some (endemics) inhabiting a single small island or group of islands (e.g. *Holacanthus limbaughi* known only from remote Clipperton Island in the eastern Pacific). Most of the nine Atlantic species occur in the western portion, commonly referred to as the West Indies or Caribbean Sea. Notable exceptions are *Holacanthus africanus* from West Africa and *Centropyge resplendens* from Ascension Island in the central Atlantic. The four species inhabiting the eastern Pacific are more closely related to western Atlantic species than those from the rest of the Indo-Pacific. This is not surprising considering that the Atlantic and eastern Pacific were interconnected until recent (geologically speaking) uplifting of the Central American land bridge closed the gap, probably in the early Pliocene epoch approximately five million years ago.

Life History

The reproductive behavior of angelfishes is relatively well known. Their fascinating habit of forming harems, found in the majority of investigated species, has attracted the attention of researchers. This phenomenon has been best studied in the smaller angelfishes, particularly those belonging to *Centropyge* and *Genicanthus*. There is little information about the spawning habits of the larger angels (e.g. *Pomacanthus*), but it appears they form pairs, although small harems have also been reported. Harems usually consist of a single male and about two to five females. Spawning occurs throughout the year in tropical areas, usually in the evening around sunset (most commonly a few minutes after sunset). However, there is minimal activity when slack water, caused by the turning of the tide, prevails.

Apolemichthys xanthotis, a harem forming species, is common in the Red Sea. Members of the harem maintain close contact while grazing algae from the rocky substrate.

Helmut Debelius/Ikan

Males initiate courtship by chasing the females for brief intervals, then swimming a short distance off the bottom, momentarily holding a static broadside display. Eventually a female is enticed to follow. The male then moves behind her and gently nuzzles the female's abdominal region with his snout. The pair then ascend well above the bottom (usually between about 3-9 m), suddenly releasing their gametes at the apex of the ascent. Both partners then quickly retreat to the bottom. The male usually spawns with each member of the harem during a single reproductive session over a period lasting about 8-10 minutes.

Eggs are positively buoyant and rise towards the surface where they float until hatching. They measure between 0.67-1.05 mm in diameter, depending on species. Larger angelfishes, such as those belonging to *Pomacanthus*, generally have the largest eggs. The incubation period is brief. Depending on the species involved and ambient temperatures, it generally ranges from about 12-24 hours. Newly-hatched larvae range in length between 1.2-2.3 mm. They have an unremarkable appearance: basically elongate and transparent with a relatively large eye, and lacking the peculiar spines and plates typical of butterflyfish larvae. The larvae are initially pelagic (remaining in the ocean's surface layer) where they are dispersed by currents. Larval duration is variable depending on species. It generally varies between 17-39 days, or roughly an average of about one month. Strangely, the species having the broadest distributions tend to have shorter pelagic stages than those, which are more localized. New recruits must run a gauntlet of predators in order to survive the highly vulnerable larva-juvenile transition period. Newly settled recruits (postlarvae) quickly assume their juvenile color pattern and seek shelter in reef crevices. The young are often fiercely territorial towards similar-sized juveniles belonging to the same species. This is understandable, as their survival depends on successfully securing and defending the retreat. There is little information on growth and maturity, but most angelfishes probably require between 1-2 years to reach sexual maturity.

Angelfishes, particularly those forming harems, are capable of female to male sex reversal. A pecking-order, or hierarchical system of dominance exists among the female members of the harem. If the male leader is devoured by a predator or experimentally removed, the dominant female gradually changes into a male, a period that usually requires between 12-20 days. In species with pronounced male-female color pattern differences (e.g. *Genicanthus*), the gonadal transformation is accompanied by the assumption of the male pattern.

Reproductive partners belonging to the same sex are sometimes in short supply, thus setting the stage for hybridization. Although this phenomenon is common among freshwater fishes, it is rarely documented in the sea. In fact, less than 60 marine fish hybrids are known. A disproportionate number of the reported cases are either angelfishes or butterflyfishes. The main reasons for their high incidence is probably related to the strong pair-bonding tendencies (especially true of many butterflyfishes and some of the larger angelfishes) and harem social structure. It's not difficult to imagine how a rare or vagrant individual, in the absence of suitable mates, might pair off with a closely related species or join a harem. Moreover, the highly visible nature of angelfishes and butterflyfishes, makes them ideal targets for observers. In other words, their unusual hybrid color patterns are far more conspicuous compared to those which might occur in other marine fishes.

Gerald R. Allen

Hybrid angelfish representing a cross between *Centropyge eibli* and *C. flavissima*. This rare individual was encountered at Christmas Island, Indian Ocean.

Richard Pyle and John Randall, ichthyologists from the Bishop Museum in Hawaii have published an extensive list of observations of angelfish hybrids. Their results indicate hybridization is a relatively common phenomenon among this family and involves most genera, although pygmy angelfishes in the genus *Centropyge* and the larger *Pomacanthus* angels are most often involved. They noted the following pairings: *Apolemichthys trimaculatus* x *A. xanthurus*, *Centropyge eibli* x *C. flavissima*, *C. eibli* x *C. vroliki*, *C. flavissima* x *C. vroliki*, *C. loricula* x *C. potteri*, *Holacanthus bermudensis* x *H. ciliaris*, *Paracentropyge multifasciata* x *C. venusta*, *Pomacanthus arcuatus* x *P. paru*, *P. chrysurus* x *P. maculosus*, *P. maculosus* x *P. semicirculatus*, and *P. sexstriatus* x *P. xanthometopon*. As well as these confirmed pairings, they reported an additional five cases of probable hybridization involving: *Centropyge bispinosa* x *C. heraldi*, *C. bispinosa* x *C. shepardi*, *Chaetodontoplus caeruleopunctatus* x *C. septentrionalis*, *C. melanosoma* x *C. septentrionalis*, and *Pomacanthus navarchus* x *P. xanthometapon*. In these latter five cases the identity of each of the last mentioned partner species was not positively confirmed, although color markings hinted of their involvement.

Angelfishes are highly dependent on the availability of shelter in the form of boulders, caves, and coral crevices. Depth range varies widely according to species, but most dwell in the reefs upper zones, usually between depths of about 2-20 meters. A number of species are restricted to much deeper water, especially some members of *Centropyge, Genicanthus,* and *Paracentropyge*, which may typically be restricted to depths below 30 m. The current depth record for the family is held by *Centropyge narcosis*, known only from depths in excess of 100 meters. Typically most species are relatively territorial, or at least can be described as home-ranging over a relatively confined section of reef. For smaller species (e.g. *Centropyge*) this may consist of only a few square meters of turf, but large angels like *Pomacanthus imperator* may occupy a range of at least 1,000 square meters. Each territory is generally inhabited by a single male and several females. During daylight the occupants forage throughout their range.

Gerald R. Allen

Shoal of Clarion Angels (*Holacanthus clarionensis*) graze algae-covered boulders at Clarion Island, Eastern Pacific Ocean.

Three main feeding types are present. Many of the smaller species, especially those in *Centropyge*, feed almost exclusively on algae. Most of the larger angelfishes (*Pomacanthus* and *Holacanthus*) consume sponges supplemented with algae and smaller amounts of zoantharians, tunicates, gorgonians, fish and invertebrate eggs, hydroids, and seagrasses. The final major feeding mode is exhibited by the species of *Genicanthus*, which form mid-water shoals that feed on zooplankton (especially pelagic tunicates), supplemented by benthic items including bryozoans, polychaetes, and algae. Perhaps not a major feeding mode, but one of the strangest reported for the family, involves Japanese *Centropyge interrupta*, which receives a significant amount of nourishment by eating the feces of plankton-feeding damselfishes (Pomacentridae) and fairy basslets (*Pseudanthias*).

Juveniles of two Indo-Pacific surgeonfishes (*Acanthurus*) are extraordinary mimics of *Centropyge* angelfishes. The young of *Acanthurus pyroferus* display a nearly faultless imitation of *Centropyge flavissima*, *C. heraldi*, and *C. vroliki*. The shape, manner of swimming, and color pattern of the mimic surgeonfish are remarkably similar to their *Centropyge* models. Likewise, *Acanthurus tristis* (a close relative of *A. pyroferus*) from the Indian Ocean, mimics *Centropyge eibli* (see photo below). The basis for this unusual mimicry remains poorly understood. Perhaps the young surgeonfish benefit from their disguise by fooling predators, who possibly avoid *Centropyge* because of their spiny (and therefore unpalatable) morphology and secretive behavior (habit of darting in out of crevices makes them an elusive prey). The mimicry is strictly confined to the juvenile stage. Once the surgeons grow beyond the maximum limit reached by the angelfishes they begin to assume the very different adult color pattern.

The juvenile of the Indian Ocean Mimic Surgeonfish, *Acanthurus tristis* (lower), has evolved a color pattern and morphology remarkably similar to that of *Centropyge eibli* (upper).

Roger Steene

Gerald R. Allen

Classification

Our classification generally follows the one proposed by Fraser-Brunner in 1933 and modified by Taiwanese ichthyologists Shen and Liu in 1979 (see list of references, page 243), but with several modifications. These were the last significant reviews of this group, which definitely requires further study. Our classification differs most noticeably in the recognition of three additional genera: *Apolemichthys*, *Desmoholacanthus*, and *Paracentropyge*. Also, we do not recognize Fraser-Brunner's *Heteropyge* (sometimes referred to as *Euxiphipops*), instead conforming with most recent authors, who generally lump it with *Pomacanthus*. A major unresolved problem involves the genus *Pomacanthus*. It may eventually be split into two (new world versus old world) or possibly three genera. This problem is currently under study by Richard Pyle as part of his PhD program at the University of Hawaii.

CHAPTER 2

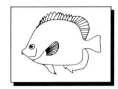 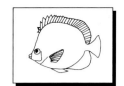 

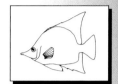

INTRODUCING BUTTERFLYFISHES

The colorful butterflyfishes are renowned for their striking patterns, delicate shapes, and graceful swimming movements. Indeed, they are arguably the reef's most conspicuous inhabitants. Scientifically known as the family Chaetodontidae (chaetodont is Latin for "bristle-tooth", referring to the fine jaw teeth). The group contains 10 genera with 116 species, the majority of which occur in tropical seas in the vicinity of coral reefs.

Morphology

Butterflyfishes have a distinctive appearance, not likely to be confused with other fishes. Only the related angelfishes have the same general shape and appearance. However, angelfishes are relatively more robust and have a sharp spine on the lower edge of the cheek. Otherwise the two families share a similar morphology, and were grouped in a single family until recent times. Butterflyfishes belong to the great suborder of modern fishes know as the Perciformes, or perch-like fishes. Like most perciforms they are difficult to characterize on the basis of a particular unique feature, rather they are best defined by a combination of characters. They have deep, compressed bodies, and small protractile mouths with brush-like teeth in the jaws. The scales are ctenoid (spiny edged) and cover the entire head and body, extending onto the median fins. The dorsal fin is composed of 6-16 sharp spines followed by 15-33 soft rays. The anal fin is similarly constructed with 3-5 spines and 15-23 soft rays.

Distribution

Nearly all butterflyfishes are found in the warm seas of the tropics. Approximately eight species are predominately subtropical (or temperate) and mainly confined to higher latitudes of Australia, South Africa, and Japan. Only two genera: *Chelmonops* (with two southern Australian species), and; *Amphichaetodon* (with another species pair from the South Pacific), are non-tropical. The vast Indo-Pacific, stretching from East Africa to the Americas, contains nearly 90% of the species. The remaining 17 species inhabit the tropical and subtropical Atlantic Ocean. Several common trends in butterflyfish distribution are apparent: (1) species that are widely distributed over major regions such as the western Pacific, Indian Ocean, or combination of the two; (2) species having a more restricted regional distribution such as Australasia (combined area of Southeast Asia and Australia), western Pacific Rim, and western Indian Ocean; and (3) endemic species, exhibiting highly restricted distributions (usually a single island or island group, or a well-defined larger region such as the Red Sea).

Opposite: Aggregation of *Chaetodon collare* from the Red Sea (Photo by John E. Randall).

14

Endemism and conservation

Although endemic species are often locally abundant, conservationists place considerable value on their occurrence. They are often used to gauge an area's biological uniqueness or as a basis for setting conservation priorities. The relatively few endemic butterflyfishes have generally evolved in remote situations...the more remote, the more endemics that are likely to be found, although the relative size of the area is also important. The Red Sea is at the top of the list as far as butterflyfish endemics are concerned. Seven species are mainly restricted there, although at least two of these have recently been found outside the Sea along the southern Arabian Peninsula, where they are considered as vagrants. Other endemic "hot spots" include Australia with six species and the Hawaiian Islands with three. The remaining 14 endemic species are widely scattered around the globe, often at tiny, remote outposts (frequently near the edge of the tropics) such as the Marquesas, Pitcairn Island, and Easter Island in the southeast corner of Polynesia, San Felix Island off Chile, Réunion in the Indian Ocean, and St. Paul's Rocks, Ascension, and St. Helena Island in the central Atlantic.

Life History

Spawning in tropical butterflyfishes probably occurs year round, but in higher latitudes such as the Hawaiian Islands and southern Japan, there is definite seasonality. At the Izu Peninsula on the Japanese island of Honshu, spawning of *Chaetodon nippon* occurs between March and October. Similar seasonality is exhibited by *C. miliaris* at Hawaii, which spawns between December and April. The belly region of gravid females becomes noticeably swollen 2-3 days prior to spawning. Courtship behavior, consisting of rapid pursuit, swimming in tight circles, and pecking or nuzzling of the female's abdomen with the male's mouth and forehead, precedes the actual release of eggs. Spawning usually occurs in the late afternoon. Pre-spawning courtship activities may involve a single female and several males, or larger groups with both sexes well represented. It culminates with pairs swimming toward the surface, well off the bottom. Sometimes the female is nudged in this direction by her partner. The spawning pair assume a side by side position as gametes are released. Additional males sometimes follow the pair upwards and shed their sperm moments after the initial gametes are released.

There is still much to be learned about the earliest life history stages of butterflyfishes. The eggs are very tiny, generally less than one millimeter in diameter. Each contains a single oil globule, which provides flotation. The eggs hatch in the open sea, presumably near the surface, approximately 24 hours after their release. The transparent larvae, which measure 2-3 mm in length, are swept along by surface currents, although they are capable of limited swimming movements. The larval duration has been studied for several species. It is possible to determine the length of time the larvae actually spend at sea before settling on the reef by microscopic examination of daily rings which form on the ear bones (otoliths). This stage of the life cycle varies greatly depending on the species involved, but generally ranges from about 19-57 days. This is similar to the larval duration of damselfishes (Pomacentridae) and the closely related angelfishes. The larvae of the Forcepsfish (*Forcipiger flavissimus*) is among the largest (>6-7 cm) in the family, no doubt an indication of its longer pelagic phase, which may last for nearly two months. It's probably no coincidence that this species is also the mostly widely distributed member of the family, ranging from East Africa to the Americas.

Butterflyfish larvae, known as *tholichthys*, are characterized by peculiar bony plates and protruding spines on the head. They are fragile organisms, primarily transparent with scattered pigment cells (melanophores) and silvery eyes. Once swept onto shallow reefs the young fish seek shelter and quickly assume the juvenile color pattern. Growth rates are variable depending on the species involved. *Chaetodon miliaris* from Hawaii grows to a total length of about 10 cm and attains sexual maturity by the end of its first year. There is little information on the longevity of butterflyfishes, but one species has lived to an age of 25 years in the Nancy Aquarium in France.

Butterflyfishes are most often seen in extensive areas of live coral, usually at depths less than about 20 m. They depend on the reef for shelter, and for their nutritional requirements. Many species feed

Gerald R. Allen

Post-larva of *Chaetodon auriga* (approx. 2 cm).

directly on the living coral polyps and others depend on an abundant supply of tiny invertebrates or pluck off bits of larger organisms such as the tube feet of echinoderms. Relatively few species are associated with adjacent habitats where coral growth is minimal. Notable exceptions include members of the Indo-Pacific genera *Chelmon* and *Parachaetodon*, which are frequently encountered on silty coastal reefs where coral diversity is low.

Butterflyfishes can be broadly categorized on the basis of their foraging and social habits. Most species are active only during daylight hours and are "home-ranging", an expression describing their daily wanderings around a limited section of reef - often an isolated patch reef or relatively small section of a more extensive reef complex. They travel throughout the territory, principally engaged in the task of feeding. A few species (*C. baronessa, C. larvatus, C. triangulum,* and *C. trifascialis*) are territorial in the strictest sense. They are closely associated with clumps of table-top *Acropora* coral, which provides shelter as well as their exclusive food supply. Individuals aggressively defend their territory, driving away other members of the same species and any other coral-feeding fishes (butterflyfishes, damsels, and wrasses).

All foraging activity ceases and butterflyfishes retreat to crevices when night envelops the reef. The only exception we know of is *Chaetodon lunula*, which regularly forges after dark. Good hiding places are at a premium and often the subject of late afternoon quarrels, although the combatants

Roger Steene

A group of *Chaetodon fasciatus* forages over a reef in the Red Sea.

16

Nocturnal color patterns of four butterflyfishes. Clockwise from upper left: *Chaetodon ephippium*, *C. trifascialis, Johnrandallia nigrirostris and C. vagabundus.*

rarely inflict damage on one another. The fish generally remain motionless through the night. Several Indo-Pacific species, including *C. aureofasciatus, C. plebius*, and *C. lunulatus*, are known to return to the same "roost" each night. Special nocturnal color patterns are evident in many species. These usually involve a general bleaching of the normal pattern or darkening of the dorsal part of the body (often accompanied by one or two pale spots).

The social behavior of butterflyfishes is a fascinating subject, which has captured the attention of several researchers. Those of you who are divers have no doubt noticed that butterflyfishes are frequently seen in pairs. Members of the pair may briefly separate while foraging, but they periodically join together. Dr. Ernst Reese of the University of Hawaii studied this behavior in detail on Australia's Great Barrier Reef and at Enewetak Atoll in the Marshall Islands. He discovered that a number of species invariably formed male-female pairs, but others were more erratic with this behavior. The first group were described as being strongly paired and the latter as weakly paired. Strongly-paired individuals often form their relationship as subadults and remain paired throughout life. Good examples of strongly paired species include *Chaetodon ephippium, C. multicinctus, C. punctatofasciatus, C. triangulum, C. baronessa, C. lunulatus, C. trifasciatus, C. unimaculatus*, and *C. vagabundus*. The weakly-paired category includes species such as *C. citrinellus, C. lunula, C. ornatissimus, C. reticulatus*, and *C. vagabundus*.

The main advantage of the pairing strategy is to ensure that a mate is always available for reproduction. In some portions of the range of a particular species, members of the same species may be in short supply, thus causing an individual to pair with another, often closely related species. This occurence is very rare, but definitely happens and mating between the dissimilar species may occur. A number of the resultant hybrids have been well documented in the scientific literature, including the progeny of these pairings: *Chaetodon argentatus* x *C. mertensii, C. auriga* x *C. ephippium, C. auriga* x *C. fasciatus, C. austriacus* x *C. melapterus, C. burgessi* x *C. tinkeri, C. burgessi* x *C. flavocoronatus, C. daedalma* x *C. nippon, C. ephippium* x *C. semion, C. guentheri* x *C. daedalma, C. kleini* x *C. unimaculatus, C. miliaris* x *C. tinkeri, C. ornatissimus* x *C. reticulatus*, and lastly *C. aureofasciatus* x *C. rainfordi*. All these hybrids are very unusual fishes, generally showing a blend of color pattern features from each of the parental species.

Photos by Roger Steene

Hybrid butterflyfishes frequently exhibit aberrant color patterns. The above examples are probable hybrids of *Chaetodon meyeri* x *C. ornatissimus* (left), and *C. punctatofasciatus* x *C. pelewensis* (right).

Not all butterflyfishes form pairs. The territorial species mentioned above are often solitary, while others band together in small groups. Among the reef's most memorable sights are butterflyfishes which form spectacular aggregations, sometimes containing several hundred fish. Among the most prominent in this respect are *Hemitaurichthys polylepis, H. zoster, Johnrandallia nigrirostris*, and *Heniochus diphreutes*. Their shoaling behavior is probably advantageous for maximum utilization of their planktonic food supply. There is also safety in numbers, an important consideration, as all of these species venture well above the safety of the bottom while feeding. The occurrence of large numbers also ensures an ample supply of reproductive partners.

There are five main feeding types in the family as determined by stomach contents of collected specimens and direct underwater observations. Species that are closely associated with rich coral growth (e.g. *C. trifasciatus, C. lunulatus, C. baronessa, C. triangulum, C. plebius,* and *C. ornatissimus*) feed predominately on hard corals (hexacorals). A second group, including *C. lineolatus, C. oxycephalus, C. melannotus, C. ocellicaudus,* and *C. unimaculatus,* feeds primarily on soft corals (octocorals), although some hard corals are consumed. The third category includes species feeding on small benthic invertebrates (excluding corals), especially polychaete worms and small crustaceans. This groups includes the species belonging to *Forcipiger* and *Chelmon,* as well as many *Chaetodon,* for example *Chaetodon auriga, C. sedentarius,* and *C. striatus.* A fourth group depends largely on zooplankton, generally feeding in large aggregation that swim high above the bottom (e.g. *Hemitaurichthys polylepis, H. zoster,* and *Heniochus diphreutes*). The fifth category contains opportunistic omnivores or generalists that feed on a wide range of items from all the above categories as well as algae.

In the Galapagos Islands, swarms of *Johnrandallia nigrirostris* commonly invade triggerfish nests to feed on the tiny eggs. The female triggerfish is unable to fend off large numbers of egg stealing predators.

Gerald R. Allen

Roger Steene

At Christmas Island, Indian Ocean, shoals of Pyramid Butterflyfish (*Hemitaurichthys polylepis*) swim high above the bottom while feeding on zooplankton

Classification

Like most other large groups of related fishes, classification of the butterflyfishes has been relatively unstable since the binomial system of nomenclature was introduced by the Swedish botanist Carole Linnaeus more than 200 years ago. The original concept of Chaetodontidae included the angelfishes as well as a host of other spiny-rayed fishes, which were long ago relegated to other families. Ernst Ahl, a German ichthyologist, published a landmark review of the family in 1923. The first truly comprehensive study, however, was that of Warren Burgess in 1978. The latter study forms the basis of our current classification, but has been modified to accommodate recent findings (both published and unpublished). The main difference between the classification used here and the one proposed by Burgess is our recognition of the genus *Prognathodes*, which Burgess recognized only as a subgenus. In addition, we recognize several species, which Burgess did not accept as distinct. Most of these involve Indian Ocean versus Pacific populations, which are very similar morphologically, but have significant color pattern differences. In some cases the Pacific and Indian Ocean forms actually occur together, providing further evidence of the distinctness. For example *Chaetodon baronessa* (Pacific) and *C. triangulum* (Indian) are seen at Bali, which lies on the boundary of these two great oceans. In the case of *C. mertensii* we have done just the opposite, recognizing only one wide ranging Indo-Pacific species, rather than including the separate Indian Ocean taxa *C. madagaskariensis*. The two were separated only on the basis of color markings, which we now know to be variable and not correlated with geography.

Opposite: A large plankton feeding shoal of *Heniochus diphreutes* (Photo by Roger Steene).

CHAPTER 3

THE INDO-WEST PACIFIC REGION

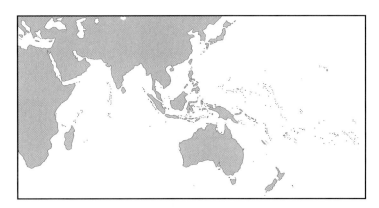

The vast Indo-west Pacific region, stretching from the Red Sea and shores of East Africa to the islands of Polynesia, is by far the world's richest marine biological province. Over three quarters of the estimated world total of 4,000 fish species inhabit this region. This includes 85% of the 205 species of angelfishes and butterflyfishes. Why is the region so incredibly biologically diverse? First and foremost is it's huge size coupled with a rich assortment of marine habitats - ranging from oceanic coral reefs to continental shores. This is the physical setting that has provided a "stage" for the impressive radiation of species. The insular nature of the region in particular - a seemingly endless variety of islands and archipelagos, have provided unparalleled opportunities for isolated speciation,

The Indo-Australian Archipelago, consisting of Indonesia, Malaysia, Philippines, New Guinea, and northern Australia, is the richest faunal province on the globe in terms of marine biodiversity. Species richness generally declines with increased distance from the center of this region, although this effect is countered by a secondary region of speciation in the Red Sea-western Indian Ocean. Australia is the world's richest area for angelfishes and butterflyfishes with 80 species. The high number reflects its huge area and favorable geographic position (straddling both temperate and tropical latitudes). The island continent's impressive tropical fauna is bolstered by elements from both the Indonesian region and Oceania.

Angelfish and Butterflyfish Hot Spots			
Location	Angels	Butterflies	Total
Taiwan	24	43	67
Great Barrier Reef	24	41	65
Flores, Indonesia	20	38	58
Komodo, Indonesia	16	37	53
Kimbe Bay, Papua New Guinea	16	34	50
Madang, Papua New Guinea	16	33	49
Manado, Indonesia	16	33	49
New Caledonia	15	33	48
Mariana Islands	16	32	48
Maldive Islands	11	32	43

Opposite: Aerial view of the Great Barrier Reef, off the coast of Queensland, Australia. (Photo by Roger Steene).

Reference List for Angelfishes and Butterflyfishes of the Indo-West Pacific Region

Apolemichthys trimaculatus
Three-Spot Angelfish
(Lacépède 1831)

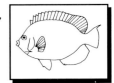

Roger Steene

Habitat Outer reef slopes and drop-offs, from 15-60 m depth. Occasionally occurs on lagoon reefs in shallower water (3-10 m).

Characters Adult: yellow overall; anal fin with broad black edge and white zone above; blue lips and dark spot on forehead. Juvenile: similar to adult, but lacking white patch and spots around head; dark spot on posterior dorsal region and narrow black band through eye extending to nape; series of golden bands on sides. Maximum size 25 cm.

Remarks Usually found solitary, or in pairs. Most likely encountered on outer reef drop-offs due to its preference for steep slopes. Diet comprised of sponges and tunicates. Name *trimaculatus* refers to the faint ocellated spot behind eye, another spot between the eyes, and a third spot on the forehead. The most common *Apolemichthys* in the Indo-Pacific region.

Distribution Widely distributed from the East African coast to Samoa, including the Indo-Australian Archipelago and Philippines. Ranges as far north as southern Japan, and south to New Caledonia.

Apolemichthys guezei
Réunion Angelfish
(Randall & Mauge 1978)

John E. Randall

Habitat Deep seaward reefs below 60 m.

Characters Dusky brown with array of golden-orange spots on scale centers; fins darker, head purplish brown, darker than body; pectoral and pelvic fins unusually long, extending to the anal fin origin and sometimes beyond; posterior portions of dorsal and anal fins distinctly angular. Maximum size about 15 cm. Resembles *Apolemichthys xanthopunctatus* (opposite) from the central Pacific, but lacks the ocelli behind the gills and on the nape.

Remarks Infrequently observed as this species tends to occur in depths not safely accessible to SCUBA divers. First collected using gill nets between 60-80 m at Réunion. It has not been recorded or collected since the type specimens were discovered in the mid-1970's.

Distribution Known only from Réunion in the western Indian Ocean, but probably also occurs at nearby Mauritius and Madagascar.

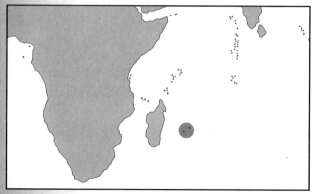

Apolemichthys xanthopunctatus
Golden-Spotted Angelfish
Burgess 1974

Helmut Debelius/Ikan

Adult

Juvenile

Richard Pyle

Habitat Vicinity of coral reefs in lagoons, on seaward reef slopes, and in channels connecting these two zones. Occurs in 3-40 m.

Characters Brown overall with golden scale centers giving spotted appearance; blue lips; black dorsal, anal and caudal fins; dark ocelli on forehead and behind gill cover. Maximum size about 25 cm. Very similar in appearance to *Apolemichthys guezei* (opposite), however these two species have widely separated geographic distributions. Additionally, *A. guezei* does not have blue lips or ocelli around the head.

Remarks Usually found either as solitary individuals, or in small groups. The Latin name translates as yellow (*xanth-*) spotted markings (*-punctatus*).

Distribution A small number of island groups in the central Pacific including the eastern Caroline (Kapingamarangi), Gilbert (Nauru, Tarawa), Phoenix (Canton), and Line Islands (Howland, Baker, Fanning).

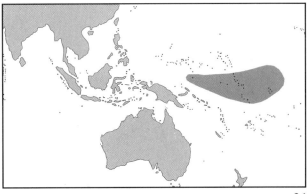

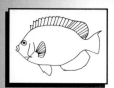

Apolemichthys xanthotis
Red Sea Angelfish
(Fraser-Brunner 1951)

★ ★

Juvenile

P. Woodhead/Ikan

H. Voigtmann/Ikan

Adult

Habitat   Vicinity of coral-rich reefs in depths between 5-35 m.

Characters   Adult: Generally pale bordered entirely by broad black markings; caudal fin pale-yellow; head darkly pigmented, this coloration ending at a level just behind pectoral fin base. Juvenile: Pale portion reduced to a small area behind pectoral fin; dark pigmentation covers posterior section of body. Reaches maximum size of 15 cm. Adult similar to *Apolemichthys xanthurus* (opposite), but dark head coloration ends before, rather than behind, pectoral fin base in that species.

Remarks   Seen commonly in pairs or small groups grazing algae, sponges and other benthic invertebrates. Scientific name translates to yellow (xanth-) ear (-ot) and refers to small yellow spot above gill cover.

Distribution   Waters adjacent to the Arabian Peninsula including Red Sea, Gulf of Aden, Oman, and Arabian Gulf.

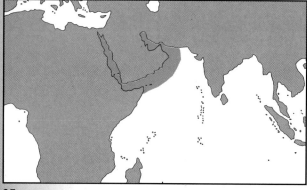

Apolemichthys xanthurus
Indian Yellow-Tail Angelfish
(Bennett 1832)

Roger Steene

Habitat   Coral reefs and rocky areas at shallow depths (5-25 m).

Characters   Body pale below becoming darker above with dark scale centers; bright yellow caudal fin; dorsal and anal fins, base of tail, and head black, forming broad dark margin around most of body; small yellow spot above gill slit. Attains maximum size of about 15 cm. Similar to *Apolemichthys xanthotis* (opposite) from the Red Sea and Arabian Peninsula, but with reduced dark head pigmentation, which ends before pectoral-fin base (ends behind pectoral fin in *A. xanthotis*).

Remarks   Found solitary or in pairs. Scientific name refers to the yellow (*xanth-*) tail (*-ur*).

Distribution   Known from scattered localities in the western Indian Ocean including Mauritius, Maldives, Sri Lanka and the east coast of India.

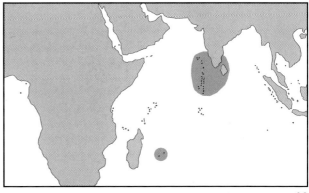

28

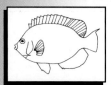

Apolemichthys griffisi
Griffis Angelfish
(Carlson & Taylor 1981)

Richard Pyle

Habitat	Steep outer reef slopes, between 10 and 60 m.
Characters	Gray overall with white band beneath black dorsal fin, extending to caudal fin base; white band bordered below by broad black marking; black blotches on nape, through eye and behind gill cover. Attains maximum size of about 25 cm.
Remarks	Generally rare, usually seen alone. The relatively recent discovery of this species, during the mid 1970's at the Gilbert Islands can be attributed to its sparse occurrence. Originally placed in the genus *Holacanthus*.
Distribution	Island groups in the central Pacific Ocean including Gilbert, Phoenix and Line islands. Also recorded from northeast Indonesia, Papua New Guinea and the Solomon Islands.

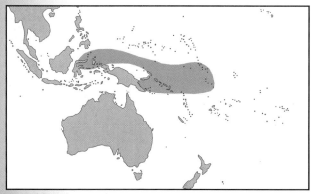

Apolemichthys kingi
Tiger Angelfish
Heemstra 1984

Adult

Phil Heemstra

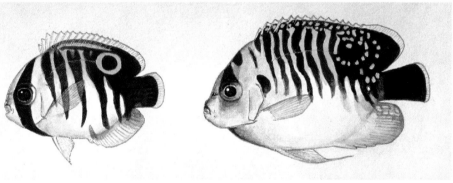

Juvenile & Sub-adult

Elaine Heemstra

Habitat Offshore reef areas, between 10 and 30 m.

Characters Distinct "tiger-like" pattern of yellow and black stripes on upper half, pale underneath; black spot behind gill cover; black caudal fin with pale margin. Reaches 20 cm in length.

Remarks Since its recent discovery (1984) an increasing number of sightings have been recorded, indicating that it may be more abundant than previously thought. The specific name honors Dennis King who first collected the species.

Distribution Between Kosi Bay and Aliwal Shoal off the southern African coast near Durban, South Africa.

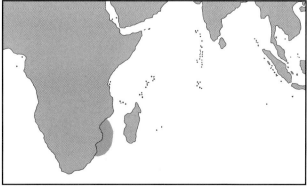

30

Apolemichthys arcuatus
Bandit Angelfish
(Gray 1831)

Ed Robinson/Ikan

Habitat Usually occurs on rocky reefs among ledges and caves, but also found in coral areas between 12-131 m depth. Most abundant between 25-50 m.

Characters Back and dorsal fin grayish, lower half of body and head white, these areas separated by broad horizontal black stripe (sometimes with distinct white margins) from head, through eye, to rear edge of dorsal fin; anal fin black with narrow white margin; broad black band (curved) covering most of outer part of caudal fin. Juveniles similar to adults. Maximum size about 18 cm.

Remarks Some recent authors place this species in a separate genus (*Desmoholacanthus*), but a recent genetic study by Chung and Woo (The Chinese University of Hong Kong, in press) confirmed it belongs in *Apolemichthys*. Feeds primarily on sponges. An incredibly docile fish easily approached and collected with hand nets without the use of anaesthetic chemicals.

Distribution Known only from the Hawaiian Islands and Johnston Island in the central Pacific.

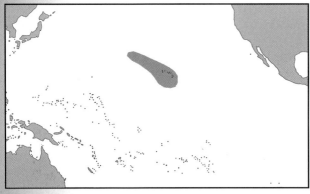

Centropyge potteri
Potter's Pygmy Angelfish
Jordan & Metz 1912

Gerald R. Allen

Habitat Rock and rubble, or coral-covered bottoms below 10 m. Juveniles sometimes found shallower.

Characters Orange-red with ornate pattern of closely spaced, broken gray vertical markings; remainder of body and fins darkly colored; vivid blue margins with horizontal black streaks on soft portions of dorsal, caudal and anal fins. Attains maximum size of about 10 cm.

Remarks Occurs solitary and is usually seen darting between crevices. Never remains away from shelter very long. When seen underwater without illumination the fish has a dull appearance; the orange-red areas appear brown or olive green, due to the invisible nature of the red end of the light spectrum below 10 m depth. Juveniles commonly seen in late spring and summer.

Distribution Common throughout the Hawaiian Islands, rare at Johnston Island.

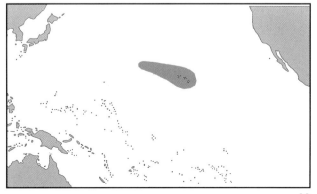

Centropyge bispinosa
Two-Spined Angelfish, Coral Beauty
(Günther 1860)

Roger Steene

Habitat	Coral reefs of lagoons and exposed outer slopes, from 5 to at least 45 m depth. Most abundant on outer reef drop-offs in deeper water.
Characters	Many color variations exist in wild populations. Usually purple or blue head, fins and adjacent body; middle section of body red-orange with numerous dark purple or blue lines. Orange coloration of body sometimes more predominant than the purple on head and fins, and dark lines may be broken into spots. Maximum size about 10 cm.
Remarks	A common species at most localities, occurring singly or in small groups, however it is very shy and never strays far from reef crevices. Interbreeds with *Centropyge shepardi* (page 55) at Guam, where it is less abundant.
Distribution	Widely dispersed in the Indo-west and central Pacific region from East Africa to the Tuamotu Islands of the South Pacific. Extends northwards to the Izu Islands off Japan, and as far south as Lord Howe Island.

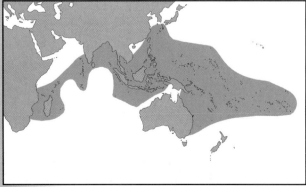

Centropyge ferrugata
Rusty Angelfish
Randall & Burgess 1972

Roger Steene

Habitat Rocky reefs and rubble areas, particularly where algae growth is extensive, between 6-30 m depth.

Characters Ground color variable (pale cream to bright red). Usually red-orange on lower half of body, becoming more dusky above with dark spots; head uniform dusky brown; margins of median fins bright blue; caudal-fin base and caudal fin rays dark. Reaches maximum size of 10 cm. *Centropyge shepardi* (page 55) is similar, but has dark bars on the sides, rather than spots which are characteristic of *C. ferrugata*.

Remarks Encountered alone or in small groups, usually observed grazing on mats of filamentous algae.

Distribution Western Pacific from southern Japan to the Philippines. Common at Okinawa.

Centropyge aurantia
Golden Angelfish
Randall & Wass 1974

Roger Steene

Habitat Occurs in rich coral areas with abundant encrusting sponges, in crevices at depths from 3-15 m, but probably also occurs deeper.

Characters Unmistakable orange coloration of entire body broken up by narrow, rippled golden bars along side; dark ring around eye; narrow dark lines on soft portions of dorsal, anal and caudal fins. Brown forms have been observed at Sulawesi, the Solomon Islands, and Pohnpei. A brown fish from the last mentioned locality turned orange in an aquarium. Maximum size about 10 cm. Could possibly be confused with *Centropyge fisheri* (page 41) which has an overlapping distribution, but that species has a dark spot near the pectoral fin.

Remarks A cryptic species inhabiting crevices on coral reefs, seldom venturing into the open. A very difficult target for underwater photographers.

Distribution Western Pacific Ocean from eastern parts of Indonesia to Papua New Guinea, Samoa and the Great Barrier Reef. North to Caroline Islands.

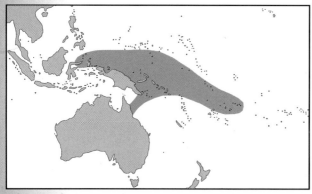

Centropyge narcosis
Deep-Reef Pygmy Angelfish
Pyle & Randall 1992

Richard Pyle

Habitat Restricted to very deep water (below 100 m) on outer reef drop-offs where it has been observed in crevices and caves on the reef wall.

Characters Entirely yellow with circular black spot near middle of body, slightly above midline. Grows to a maximum size of about 8 cm. Juveniles of *Centropyge flavissima* (page 45) and *Holacanthus tricolor* (page 210) are similar, but the spot on the side has a blue edge in both of these species.

Remarks First collected at the Cook Islands in 1989 at a depth of 110 m by aquarium fish collector Charles Boyle using quinaldine (a fish anesthetic) and hand nets. The only angelfish known to be restricted to such extreme depths. Has been observed singly and in small groups. When threatened, orients itself vertically. In this position the black spots on the sides resemble eyes of a much larger fish. The scientific name refers to the extreme effects of nitrogen narcosis experienced while collecting the first specimens using conventional SCUBA.

Distribution So far known only from the Cook Islands. Known range will probably expand with further exploration of deep reefs at other locations.

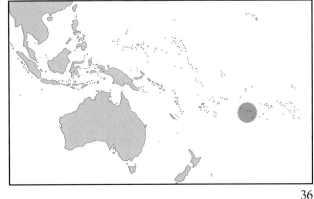

Centropyge debelius
Blue Mauritius Angelfish
Pyle 1990

Helmut Debelius/Ikan

Habitat Steep outer reef drop-offs, especially where vertical walls are covered with algae. In depths from 48-90 m.

Characters Face, breast, pelvic and pectoral fins and adjacent area of body yellow; remainder of body brilliant blue; caudal fin yellow; series of black spots on blue section of head and adjacent part of body, gradually fading posteriorly. Reaches maximum size of 9 cm. Similar color pattern to *Centropyge nahackyi* (opposite), but that species has a series of black bars, rather than spots, on the blue section of the head.

Remarks A rare species, infrequently sighted by divers. One of the most recently discovered angelfishes, first observed and photographed by German photographer Helmut Debelius in 1988. The species was later collected and named in his honor.

Distribution Recorded only from Mauritius and Réunion, in the southwest Indian Ocean.

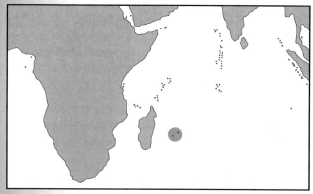

Centropyge nahackyi
Nahacky's Pygmy Angelfish
Kosaki 1989

Habitat Deep outer reef slopes from 25-70 m, usually on rubble substrates.

Characters Face and breast (including pectoral and pelvic fins) yellow; remainder of body dark blue; several black bars on blue background above and posterior to eye; yellow caudal region. Maximum size reached 9 cm. Color pattern most similar to *C. debelius* (opposite) from Mauritius and Réunion in the Indian Ocean, which has spots above the eye, rather than bars. *Centropyge multicolor* (page 51) is also similar, but much paler overall.

Remarks Little information exists for this species, which apparently forms aggregations on rubble substrates.

Distribution Mainly Johnston Atoll in the central Pacific, but strays to Hawaiian Islands.

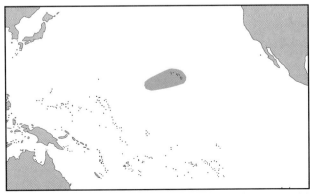

Centropyge eibli
Eibl's Angelfish
Klausewitz 1963

★ ★ ★

Roger Steene

Habitat Most frequently encountered in rich coral areas, between 3-25 m.

Characters Overall pale gray with numerous thin brown or orange bars on sides; black caudal fin. Juvenile similar to adult. Maximum size about 11 cm.

Remarks Closely related to *Centropyge vroliki* (opposite) and hybrids of these two species are occasionally encountered in the wild. Also hybridizes with *C. flavissima* (page 45) at Christmas Island in the eastern Indian Ocean. Juveniles of the surgeonfish *Acanthurus tristis* mimic the color pattern and behavior of *C. eibli* (see page 12). Subtle differences in shape and appearance of the snout, eye and body serve to distinguish the two.

Distribution Eastern Indian Ocean, northwestern Australia, through Indonesia as far east as Flores.

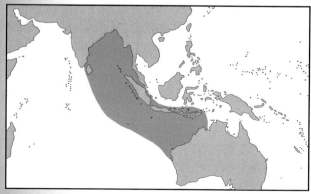

Centropyge vroliki
Pearl-Scaled Angelfish
(Bleeker 1853)

Roger Steene

Habitat Lagoon reefs and outer slopes, most frequently on rock or rubble bottoms with prolific growth of algae and encrusting sponges. Ranges in depth between 1-25 m.

Characters Mostly pale tan or gray, grading to black at rear; iris, pectoral fin base, and margin of gill cover orange; adults with vivid blue margin on darker portions of fins. Reaches maximum size of 12 cm.

Remarks Most common member of the genus in the Australia-New Guinea region. Closely related to both *Centropyge eibli* (opposite) and *C. flavissima* (page 45) and forms hybrids with both of these species. Mimicked by the juvenile of the surgeonfish *Acanthurus pyroferus*. Feeds mostly on algae and sponges.

Distribution Indo-west Pacific region from Christmas Island, throughout Indo-Australian Archipelago, to Vanuatu and Marshall Islands. South to Lord Howe Island and north to southern Japan.

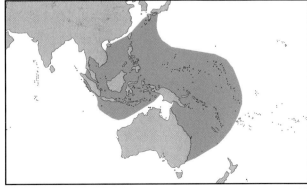

Centropyge fisheri
Fisher's Pygmy Angelfish
(Snyder 1904)

John E. Randall

Habitat   Coral rubble, especially on outer reef slopes. Ranges in depth from 10-85 m.

Characters   Orange with a black blotch behind the pectoral fin; edge of soft dorsal and anal fin blue; caudal fin pale yellow. Juveniles similar to adults. Grows to about 6 cm.

Remarks   Common below 30 m depth. A secretive fish which has the appearance and habits typical of a damselfish (Pomacentridae). There is experimental evidence for male to female sex change. Closely related to the widely distributed *Centropyge flavicauda* (opposite). Some researchers consider the two as subspecies of *C. fisheri*, but we prefer to recognize them as separate species based on distinctive color pattern differences.

Distribution   Hawaiian Islands and Johnston Island (rare).

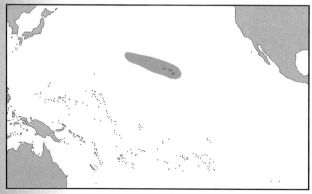

Centropyge flavicauda
White-Tail Pygmy Angelfish
Fraser-Brunner, 1933

Habitat Coral rubble of lagoon channels and outer reef slopes at depths between 10-60 m.

Characters Dark blue to nearly back with contrasting white or pale yellow caudal fin. Juveniles similar to adults. Reaches maximum length of 6 cm.

Remarks Usually common wherever it occurs. A secretive fish, which darts quickly in and out of rubble crevices. Usually seen alone, but may be many others in the general vicinity. Closely related to and considered by some to be synonymous with *C. fisheri* (opposite).

Distribution Occurs throughout Indo-west and central Pacific from East Africa to the Tuamotu Archipelago, north to southern Japan and south to the Great Barrier Reef.

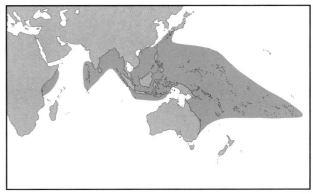

Centropyge flavipectoralis
Yellowfin Pygmy Angelfish
Randall & Klausewitz 1977

John E. Randall

Habitat Areas of coral rubble, and on margins of reefs in 3-20 m depth.

Characters Overall dark coloration of entire body and head; distinctive yellow pectoral fins. Maximum size 10 cm. Similar in appearance to *Centropyge multispinis* (opposite), but the two can be easily separated on the basis of pectoral fin coloration.

Remarks Originally collected in Sri Lankan waters in 1955, this species was thought to be the same as *C. multispinis* but was eventually described as a separate species after further collections were made during the 1970's. Usually occurs singly. Scientific name refers to the distinctive yellow (*flavi-*) pectoral fins (*-pectoralis*).

Distribution Sri Lanka and the Maldives to the Andaman Sea.

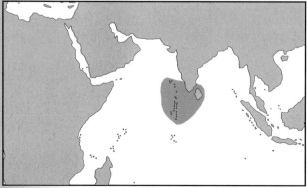

Centropyge multispinis
Many-Spined Angelfish
(Playfair & Günther 1867)

Roger Steene

Habitat Usually rubble bottoms near coral reefs, but also found among coral in lagoons and on outer reefs from 1-30 m.

Characters Body entirely dusky brown with darkened bars on sides; fins with blue markings (particularly noticeable on pelvics); blue-edged dark spot above gill cover. Maximum size attained 9 cm. Superficially resembles *Centropyge flavipectoralis* (opposite), which has overlapping distribution, but easily distinguished by difference in pectoral fin coloration.

Remarks Most abundant member of the genus in the Indian Ocean, particularly common at Maldives and Chagos Archipelago. Very approachable underwater. Rare color variations recorded which have patches of yellow-orange on the body. Formerly placed in the subgenus *Xiphypops*, but a recent Japanese study revealed it belongs in *Centropyge*.

Distribution Throughout western and northern Indian Ocean from East African coast and Red Sea to western Thailand. Questionable record from Australia's north coast, off Darwin.

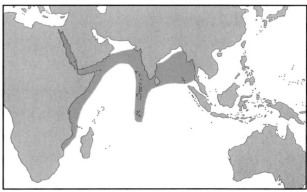

Centropyge flavissima
Lemonpeel Angelfish
(Cuvier 1831)

Juvenile

Adult

Roger Steene

Roger Steene

Habitat   Coral rich areas of lagoons and seaward reefs, occasionally in surge channels. Most common in shallows (above 20 m), but also occurs below 25 m.

Characters   Adult: Bright yellow head and body; light blue markings around eye, on edge of gill cover, on cheek spine, and on margins of soft portions of dorsal, anal, and caudal fins. Juvenile: Same as adult, but with a blue-rimmed ocellus on the sides. Reaching maximum size of 14 cm. *Centropyge heraldi* (opposite) is similar, but lacks the blue markings described above.

Remarks   Usually occurs in harem groups. Can undergo male to female sex change, taking 2-3 months. Feeds mostly on filamentous algae. Closely related to *Centropyge eibli* (page 39) and *C. vroliki* (page 40) forming hybrids with both. Mimicked by juvenile surgeonfish (*Acanthurus pyroferus*). Populations from Christmas and Cocos-Keeling Islands have slightly different markings around the head and eye and may possibly represent a separate species.

Distribution   Widespread but fragmented range from Christmas and Cocos-Keeling Islands in the East-

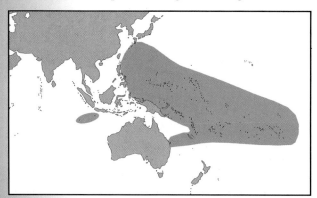

ern Indian Ocean to the Marquesas and Ducie Island in the South Pacific. North to the Ryukus, and south to New Caledonia and Rapa. Common throughout Micronesia (except Palau and Yap). Uncommon in Indo-Australian Archipelago, Caroline Islands, and at Easter Island.

Centropyge heraldi
Herald's Angelfish
Woods & Schultz 1953

John E. Randall

Habitat Outer reef slopes, between 8-40 m, but also encountered on shallower lagoon reefs.

Characters Entire body and head bright yellow; small dusky patch with yellow spots behind eye. Maximum size about 10 cm. Very similar in appearance to *Centropyge flavissima* (opposite), but lacks blue markings . Also, rear portions of dorsal and anal fins are slightly more angular in *C. heraldi*.

Remarks Color variants with a broad black margin on the soft portion of the dorsal fin are sometimes observed in the wild.

Distribution Central and western Pacific, from southern Japan and Taiwan to the Tuamotu Islands. South to the Great Barrier Reef. Apparently does not occur at Palau or Yap.

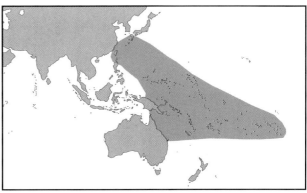

Centropyge hotumatua
Hotumatua's Angelfish
Randall & Caldwell 1973

John E. Randall

Habitat Rocky or coral reef areas with abundant crevices, in depths between 14-45 m.

Characters Head and breast (to anal fin origin) orange-yellow; remainder of body deep blue; caudal fin and its base yellow-orange; small dark spot near gill cover, and blue ring around eye. Maximum size 8 cm. Similar in color to *Centropyge joculator* (opposite) and *C. bicolor* (page 49), however these species are not found within the range occupied by *C. hotumatua*, which can be distinguished by more rounded soft portions of the dorsal and anal fins, and the more distinctly orange head.

Remarks The scientific name is derived from the legendary Polynesian chieftain Hotumatua, who first colonized Easter Island.

Distribution Scattered remote islands in the South Pacific (Austral, Rapa, Pitcairn, and Easter Island).

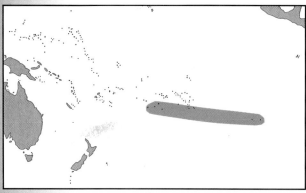

Centropyge joculator
Cocos Pygmy Angelfish
Smith-Vaniz & Randall 1974

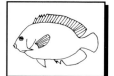

Gerald R. Allen

Habitat Coral or rubble areas on steep outer reef slopes and drop-offs from 15 to at least 70 m depth. Sometimes as shallow as 8 m above steep drop-offs.

Characters Body broken into two clearly demarcated color zones - yellow anteriorly and dark blue behind; caudal fin yellow; blue ring around eye. Reaches a maximum size of about 9 cm. Resembles *Centropyge bicolor* (page 49), but lacks blue bar above eye.

Remarks Occurs either singly or in small groups of up to about 5-6 individuals. Males have slightly elongated rear portions of the dorsal and anal fins respective to females. Most closely related to *Centropyge hotumatua* (opposite) from the south Pacific. The name *joculator* means jester or clown, and refers to its bright, gaudy coloration.

Distribution Known only from Cocos-Keeling Island and Christmas Island (where it is common) in the eastern Indian Ocean.

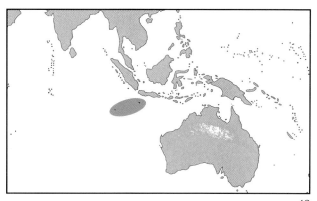

Centropyge bicolor
Bicolor Angelfish
(Bloch 1787)

Roger Steene

Habitat	Areas of rich coral growth on seaward reefs, drop-offs and in lagoons. Also occurs in rubble areas. Most commonly observed between 10-25 m, but also seen in shallower water.
Characters	Head and front of body bright yellow; dark blue posteriorly; caudal fin yellow; blue bar extending vertically from eye to forehead. Maximum size reached 15 cm. Similar blue and yellow coloration is evident in *Centropyge joculator* (page 48), but that species lacks a blue bar above the eye.
Remarks	Common throughout most of its range, but rare at Palau to eastern Caroline, Mariana, and Marshall islands. Swims close to the bottom grazing on algae never straying far from shelter of reef crevices. Occurs singly, in pairs, or in small aggregations.
Distribution	Indo-west and central Pacific, from Malaysia to Polynesia (Phoenix Is., Samoa), north to southern Japan, and south to New Caledonia, Great Barrier Reef and northwestern Australia.

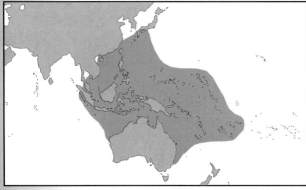

Centropyge interrupta
Japanese Pygmy Angelfish
(Tanaka 1918)

Male

John E. Randall

Roger Steene

Female

Captive male (Midway Is.)

Gerald R. Allen

Habitat Rocky shores, from 15 to at least 60 m depth. Also found in areas of moderate coral growth.

Characters Females: Head and front of body orange-red, dotted with blue markings (see Chapter 2, page 7); rear of body grading to dark blue; caudal fin base orange and fin yellow. Males: Overall body coloration much paler than female; region of gill cover with heavy blue lines making head appear blue overall; rear margin of dorsal and anal fins blue with numerous horizontal black markings. Juveniles have a blue-rimmed ocellus on soft dorsal fin. Attains 15 cm.

Remarks Only species in the genus with distinct color differences between sexes. Reproductive habits known to involve sex reversal. Color pattern fades after long periods in captivity, and blue color is largely replaced by orange.

Distribution Northwestern Pacific Ocean. Along Japan's southern coast extending from Tosa Bay (Shikoku) to Tokyo (Honshu), particularly common at Izu Peninsula. Range extends south to Izu and Bonin Islands and northeast to the outlying Hawaiian Islands of Midway and Kure (relatively rare).

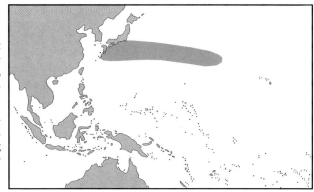

Centropyge multicolor
Multicolor Pygmy Angelfish
Randall & Wass 1974

John E. Randall

Habitat Steep outer reef slopes and drop-offs in deep water between 20-90 m, usually among coral rubble or under ledges.

Characters Whitish, becoming dusky golden ventrally; yellow face and breast; dorsal and anal fins blue with darkly colored markings; characteristic blue patch with black bars above eye; yellow caudal fin. Maximum size approximately 9 cm. Similar to *Centropyge nahackyi* (page 38), but distinguished by its overall paler coloration.

Remarks Shy species, very secretive in the wild, preferring to remain close to shelter.

Distribution Numerous island groups throughout western and central Oceania including Palau, Carolines (abundant at Pohnpei), Gilbert, Fiji, Cook and Society Islands. One specimen was recorded from the Hawaiian Islands.

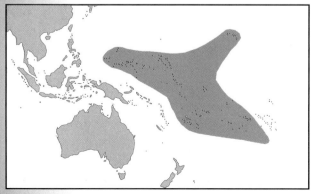

Centropyge nigriocella
Black-Spot Pygmy Angelfish
Woods & Schultz 1953

Richard Pyle

Habitat	Coral rubble in lagoons, and on outer reefs from depths of 4-15 m.
Characters	Pale overall; silver-rimmed black ocellus on soft dorsal fin; black marking at base of pectoral fin. Maximum size about 6 cm.
Remarks	A very shy, cryptic species yet to be observed in the field. Not yet widely available in the aquarium hobby. Known mainly on the basis of collections made using chemicals.
Distribution	Scattered locations in the central and western Pacific including Johnston Island, Line Islands (Fanning), Mariana, Admiralty, and Samoan Islands.

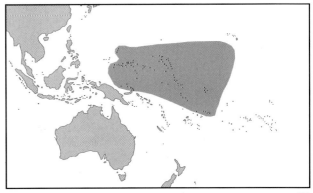

Centropyge nox
Midnight Angelfish
(Bleeker 1853)

★ ★

Roger Steene

Habitat Rich coral areas and rubble bottoms, most commonly on sheltered outer reefs, but also in lagoons and passages. Occupies depths from 10 to at least 70 m.

Characters Uniformly black over entire body, head and fins. Maximum size reached is 9 cm. Easily distinguished from other blackish *Centropyge* (e.g. *C. flavicauda*, page 42 and *C. tibicen*, opposite), by its solid coloration.

Remarks A secretive species which rapidly retreats to shelter in the form of cracks and crevices when disturbed. Remains close to shelter at all times.

Distribution Western Pacific from Ryukyu Islands, Palau, Caroline Islands (Kapingamarangi), southwards throughout Melanesia to the Great Barrier Reef (not abundant) and New Caledonia.

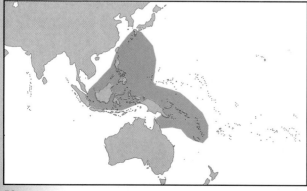

Centropyge tibicen
Keyhole Angelfish
(Cuvier 1831)

Roger Steene

Habitat Coral and rubble areas in lagoons and on seaward reefs, from 4-35 m depth.

Characters Dark blue overall with white marking on upper side behind pectoral fin; yellow margin on ventral fins. Largest member of genus, reaching maximum size of 18 cm.

Remarks Distributed over a relatively wide area, but is never particularly abundant. Usually seen alone or in small groups. Forms harems consisting of single male and several females. Diet comprised primarily of algae.

Distribution Indo-west Pacific region from northwest Australian coast and Christmas Island, throughout Indo-Australian Archipelago to New Caledonia. North to southern Japan, and south to Lord Howe Island.

Centropyge shepardi
Shepard's Pygmy Angelfish
Randall & Yasuda 1979

★ ★

John E. Randall

Habitat   Exposed outer reefs on mixed substrata of living and dead corals, between 10-56 m. Sometimes encountered in coral-rich areas of lagoons.

Characters   Orange-red to orange-yellow with variable number of black bars (usually more than 5, occasionally absent); dusky orange forehead, dorsal surface and soft portions of dorsal and anal fins; median fins with blue margin, streaked with black markings on rear edge (more pronounced in males); caudal fin pale to transparent. Grows to maximum length of 12 cm. *Centropyge loricula* (opposite) is similar, but is more brightly colored and generally has five well defined black bars on the side.

Remarks   Occurring either singly or in small aggregations (harems) where one male associates with several smaller females. Capable of sex reversal. Hybridizes with *C. bispinosa* (page 33) at Guam.

Distribution   Western Pacific Ocean at Mariana and Bonin Islands, extending north to the Izu Islands.

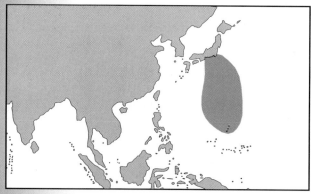

Centropyge loricula
Flame Angelfish
(Günther 1874)

Roger Steene

Habitat From 5-60 m depth in rich coral areas on seaward and lagoonal reefs.

Characters Unmistakable striking color pattern. Red-orange body, interior more orange-yellow with series of five broad black bars, becoming broken at dorsal fin (bars occasionally absent); rear edge of dorsal and anal fins black with horizontal blue streaks (more pronounced in males). Reaches maximum size of 10 cm. *Centropyge shepardi* (opposite) is similar, but has more, less-defined dark bars on the sides.

Remarks One of the most popular angelfishes in the aquarium hobby. Quickly adapts to captivity and exceptionally hardy. Displays secretive behavior in the wild, staying close to shelter.

Distribution Scattered localities in the western Pacific from Palau to Marquesas, Hawaiian Islands, and Ducie Island, southwards to the Great Barrier Reef. Rare in Indonesia, most common at Palau, Caroline, Marshall, and Society Islands.

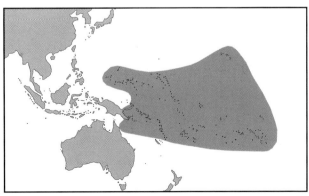

56

Centropyge acanthops
African Pygmy Angelfish
(Norman 1922)

Gerald R. Allen

Habitat   Coral and rubble areas, usually between 8-40 m depth. Prefers substrates with a thick cover of algae.

Characters   Bright orange from head to behind pectoral fin, extending along back and dorsal fin; remainder of body dark blue; caudal fin yellow, almost transparent. Reaches maximum size of about 8 cm. Similar in appearance to juveniles and sub-adults of the western Atlantic Pygmy Angelfish, *Centropyge aurantonota* (page 202), which are distinguished by the dark blue caudal fin.

Remarks   Also known as the jumping bean in parts of Africa, this species is closely related to the widely distributed *Centropyge fisheri* (page 41), although the two have dissimilar color patterns. Japanese researchers have demonstrated male to female sex change in this species. Occurs alone or in small groups of up to about 10 individuals.

Distribution   Coastal East Africa from Somalia to South Africa. Also known from Mauritius, Seychelles, Mascarene Islands, the Chagos Archipelago, and off the coast of Oman.

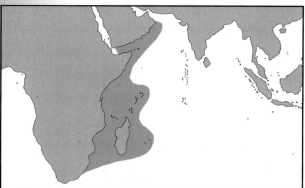

Robert Halstead

Habitat   A seldom seen species inhabiting crevices and caves on steep outer reef slopes, from 25 to at least 75 m depth.

Characters   Entirely yellow except for broad patch of blue extending from forehead along the dorsal fin and adjacent body, terminating just before the posterior-most section of the soft dorsal fin; dark blue ring around eye. Attains 9 cm.

Remarks   Extremely uncommon species which, due to its secretive behavior and preference for deep water, is rarely sighted by divers. Apparently has no close relatives.

Distribution   Previously thought to be restricted to the Cocos-Keeling Islands in the northeast Indian Ocean. Now known to occur also at Palau, Papua New Guinea, Indonesia, Marshall Islands, Fiji and Guam.

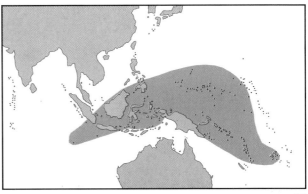

Chaetodontoplus septentrionalis
Blue-Stripe Angelfish
(Temminck & Schlegel 1844)

★ ★

Roger Steene

Habitat Rocky or coral-covered coastal reefs, between 5-60 m.

Characters Adult: Brownish orange with numerous horizontal blue stripes on head, body and median fins; pelvic and caudal fins yellow. Juvenile: Small juveniles mostly black with yellow band behind head, and yellow caudal fin; blue stripes appear at a length of about 4 cm. Attains 20 cm. Juveniles similar to those of *Chaetodontoplus melanosoma* (page 69), but without black on caudal fin. Also similar to *C. personifer* (page 65) and *C. meredithi* (page 66), however confusion with these species is unlikely as they are not found in the same localites..

Remarks Color pattern similarities and the co-occurance of *C. septentrionalis* and *C. chrysocephalus* (opposite) have caused speculation that the two may be variations of a single species, *chrysocephalus* possibly representing the mature male of *C. septentrionalis*.

Distribution Western Pacific, from southern China and Taiwan, north to southern Japan.

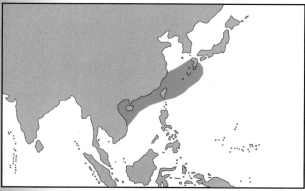

Chaetodontoplus chrysocephalus
Orange-Faced Angelfish
Bleeker 1854

Tomonori Hirata

Habitat Areas of mixed substrata, including coral and rocky reefs, rubble, and sand in 1-30 m, but most common in about 15-25 m.

Characters Dusky brown body, darkening posteriorly; yellow-orange face; irregular narrow blue markings more prominent on head and anterior section of body; rear edge of dorsal and anal fins, and entire caudal fin yellow. Attains 22 cm length. Similar to *Chaetodontoplus septentrionalis*, but the narrow blue markings are more prominent over the entire body in that species.

Remarks Relatively common at Kashiwa-jima off southern Japan (Shikoku I.), also encountered on west side of Izu Peninsula (Honshu I.), but in smaller numbers. Possibly a variant of *C. septentrionalis* (opposite) or possibly the male of that species. No juveniles (smaller than 8 cm) have been observed or collected, which supports this contention. Furthermore, the distributions of these two species are practically identical. Another theory put forward by Pyle and Randall is that it represents a hybrid between *C. melanosoma* (page 63) and *C. septentrionalis*.

Distribution Western Pacific region, from Sagami Bay, Japan to Indonesia (Java) .

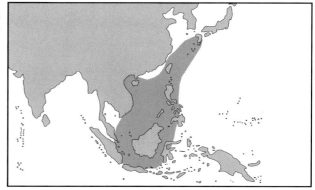

Chaetodontoplus conspicillatus
Conspicuous Angelfish
(Waite 1900)

Roger Steene

Habitat Outer reefs between 20-40 m. Juveniles frequently seen shallower in lagoons, harbors or protected bays, especially in areas of abundant soft coral.

Characters Adult: Dusky underneath, becoming blue-gray above; dorsal and anal fins with broad dark border and pale margin; yellow on face and basal part of caudal and pectoral fins, which are black otherwise; blue margin on gill cover and cheek, also blue ring around eye. Juvenile: Black overall, pale (greenish) dorsally. Maximum size about 25 cm.

Remarks A spectacular fish commanding high prices in the aquarium trade.

Distribution Southern Coral Sea, southern Great Barrier Reef and adjacent coast, south to central New South Wales (Australia). Also recorded from New Caledonia, Lord Howe and Norfolk Island.

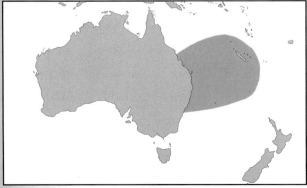

Chaetodontoplus duboulayi
Scribbled Angelfish
(Günther 1867)

Roger Steene

Habitat Shallow coastal and continental shelf reefs, commonly on open flat bottom areas, or on rock and coral-covered substrates. Usually no deeper than 20 m.

Characters Mostly dark blue with ornate, narrow light blue horizontal markings on body and median fins; broad yellow bar behind pectoral fin base, encompassing pelvic and pectoral fins; another broad yellow marking lies below base of dorsal fin, extending onto caudal fin; variable sized white patch encompassing gill cover; yellow snout. Reaches maximum size of about 25 cm.

Remarks Commonly found in pairs or small groups, sometimes solitary. Feeds mainly on sponges and tunicates. White patch on gill cover sometimes more apparent in male specimens.

Distribution Coastal regions of northern Australia from northwest Western Australia to Queensland. Also found in southern parts of Indonesia, the Aru Islands and southern New Guinea.

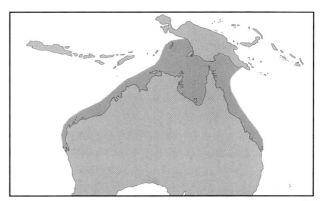

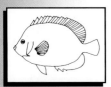

Chaetodontoplus caeruleopunctatus
Blue-Spotted Angelfish
Yasuda & Tominaga 1976

Helmut Debelius/Ikan

Habitat Unknown, but probably occurs on coastal reefs.

Characters Ground color varies, either dark or faded bluish brown with many small light blue spots (absent from head); soft portions of dorsal and anal fins darker than rest of body, with white margin; bright yellow caudal fin. Maximum size about 14 cm.

Remarks Information on the ecology and behavior of this species is lacking. Scientific name refers to the distinct color pattern of blue (*caeruleo-*) spots (*-punctatus*).

Distribution Possibly restricted to the Philippine Archipelago. Has been collected at Cebu Island.

Chaetodontoplus niger
Black Angelfish
Chan, 1969

Jill Ruse

Habitat The four known specimens were captured at depths between 20-80 meters, over a mixed bottom of corals, rocks and muddy sand.

Characters Adult: Head, body and median fins entirely jet black; pelvic fins and adjacent breast region white; caudal fin abruptly bright lemon yellow on rear edge. Juvenile (about 6 cm length): Entirely black with purple tint except for light yellow pelvic fins (and adjacent breast) and rear half of caudal fin; relatively broad black submarginal band along posterior edge of caudal fin, upper and lower ends extending forward to about middle of fin - this black band and its forward extensions bordered by fine white margin. Adult specimens from Japan have a slight yellowish tinge on the outer edge of the spinous dorsal fin and blackish outer edge on the caudal fin. Estimated maximum size is 30-35 cm.

Remarks An extremely rare species known on the basis of only four specimens. Three of these were collected in 1994 from Japan. This species has not been observed underwater, all specimens were captured by trawling.

Distribution Known so far only from Macclesfield Bank (16°4.8'N, 114°40.8E), midway between Viet Nam and the Philippines, and from Wakeyama Prefecture, southern Honshu, Japan.

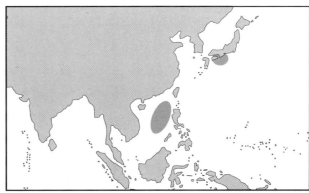

Chaetodontoplus personifer
Western Yellow-Tail Angelfish
(McCulloch 1914)

Gerald R. Allen

Habitat Coastal reefs and nearby flat bottoms with rocky or coral-covered outcrops, between depths of 10-40 m.

Characters Adult: Black body and median fins; yellow forehead, breast and pelvic fins; caudal fin mostly black with yellow on rear edge; blue face with yellow spots; white patch posterior to head. Juvenile: Entirely black except for broad white bar behind head and yellow pelvic and caudal fins. Maximum size 35 cm. Juvenile identical to that of *Chaetodontoplus meredithi* (opposite). Adults of these species also very similar, but separable on the basis of caudal fin coloration (mostly black in *C. personifer*) and maximum size (considerably greater in *C. personifer*).

Remarks Males are slightly more elongate than females. Only recently recognized as a valid species. Formerly united with *C. meredithi*. They are closely related and share almost identical ecological requirements.

Distribution Western Australia, north of the Abrolhos Islands.

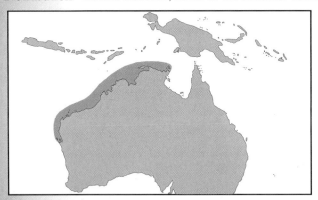

Chaetodontoplus meredithi
Queensland Yellow-Tail Angelfish
Kuiter 1990

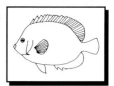

Habitat Coastal reefs on open flat bottoms with rock and coral patches, frequently with sponge and seawhip growth. Adults usually deeper than 30 m, but juveniles often seen shallower on protected inner reefs and around jetties.

Characters Adult: Black body and median fins; yellow forehead, breast, pelvic fins and caudal fin (black margin); blue face with yellow spots, white patch behind; mouth black. Juvenile: Entirely black except broad white bar behind head and yellow pelvic and caudal fins. Maximum size 25 cm. Juvenile virtually identical to that of *Chaetodontoplus personifer* (opposite). Adults of these two species also very similar, but distinguished by caudal fin coloration (more yellow in *C. meredithi*).

Remarks Relatively uncommon, occurring singly or paired. Feeds primarily on sponges and tunicates. Only recently separated from *C. personifer*, the two having long been considered a single species. The broad yellow marking behind the gill cover of juveniles is similar to that seen in juveniles of *C. melanosoma* (page 69) and *C. septentrionalis* (page 60).

Distribution Eastern Australia from Queensland (rare on the Great Barrier Reef) to New South Wales (Sydney). Also at Lord Howe Island.

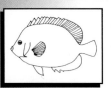

Chaetodontoplus mesoleucus
Vermiculated Angelfish
(Bloch 1787)

Roger Steene

Adult (yellow tailed form)

Roger Steene

Adult (gray tailed form)

Habitat Areas of rich coral growth on silty inner coastal reefs and lagoons, usually between 1-20 m.

Characters Triangular white patch behind head (edge passes from dorsal fin origin to anal fin origin) grading to dark color on posterior half of body; black bar through eye; yellow snout, forehead and anterior section of dorsal fin; caudal fin yellow or gray. Maximum size 18 cm.

Remarks An unusual species, which resembles a butterflyfish, but has the distinctive cheek spine of angelfishes. Further taxonomic study may result in its placement in a separate genus, as well as the recognition of two distinct species (on the basis of caudal fin color). Adults occur alone or in pairs and at some locations (e.g. Pulau Bintan, near Singapore) are easily approached at close range. Feeds on sponges, tunicates and algae.

Distribution Western Pacific, throughout southeast Asia to New Guinea and the Solomon Islands, also relatively common along the Kimberley coast of northwestern Australia. Range extends north to the Ryukyu Islands, through Palau.

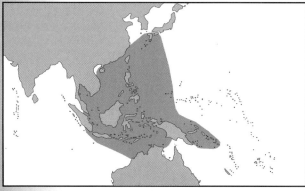

Chaetodontoplus ballinae
Ballina Angelfish
Whitley 1959

Peter Parker

Habitat   Coral and rocky reefs between 10-80 m depth.

Characters   Pearly gray overall with broad black marking (sometimes covering entire upper half of body) commencing at pectoral fin, extending to caudal-fin base; black markings through eye and also on mouth; eye, pectorals and caudal fin distinctly yellow. Juvenile has not been observed in the wild. Reaches maximum size of at least 20 cm.

Remarks   Previously known from only two specimens captured in 60-80 m at Ballina, New South Wales - recently rediscovered on top of a seamount, a few kilometers off Lord Howe Island. Here it is common in shallower water (15-20 m) over rocky substrate with patches of coral (*Acropora*). One of the most infrequently sighted angelfishes in the world and one of only a few species in the family yet to be found in the aquarium hobby. The photograph is the first ever taken in the natural habitat.

Distribution   Northern New South Wales (Coffs Harbour, Ballina, North Solitary Islands) and Lord Howe Island.

Chaetodontoplus melanosoma
Black Velvet Angelfish
(Bleeker 1853)

John E. Randall

Habitat Coastal and outer reef areas often in areas of cool upwellings, from 5-30 m depth.

Characters Adult: Mostly black with large patch of pale gray along back and upper half of body (PNG specimens with pale gray restricted to head); rear edge of dorsal, caudal and anal fins yellow; head pale yellow-orange. Juvenile: Dark with curved yellow bar behind head and broad yellow border on soft portions of fins; caudal fin yellow with central black patch. Maximum size attained about 20 cm. Juveniles similar to those of *Chaetodontoplus septentrionalis* (page 60), *C. meredithi* (page 66) and *C. personifer* (page 65).

Remarks Usually seen alone. Several color variants exist involving differences in caudal fin coloration. Caudal fin either black with yellow rear margin, yellow with enclosed central black patch, or entirely yellow (southern Japan). Possibly two or more species involved - additional research required to confirm status of variants.

Distribution Throughout Indonesia (common on southern half of Komodo Island) and Philippines to New Guinea (Milne Bay Province). Range extends north to southern Japan.

Genicanthus bellus
Ornate Angelfish
Randall 1975

Male

Helmut Debelius/Ikan

Female

Michale Moxter/Ikan

Habitat   Steep outer reef slopes and drop-offs between 25-100 m, uncommon in less than 50 m.

Characters   Female: Overall white with broad black stripe from back of head to lower edge of caudal fin, upper edge of caudal fin also black; orange markings on anal and dorsal fins; other dark markings on forehead, behind head, and on base of dorsal fin; two pinkish markings on body. Male: White body with orange mid-lateral stripe and another on forehead, continued along dorsal fin base; orange blotches on tail base and caudal fin. Attains 18 cm.

Remarks   Forms small aggregations which feed on plankton. Groups swim about five meters off the bottom and are quick to retreat to the safety of the reef when approached. Females are larger than males at maturity. Spawning occurs 15-30 minutes after sunset. Eggs measure 0.7 mm in diameter and hatch in about 15 hours.

Distribution   Scattered localities mainly in the western Pacific, including the Society Islands (Tahiti), Marianas, Marshalls, and Philippines. Also recorded from Cocos-Keeling Atoll in the eastern Indian Ocean. Probably more widespread, but undetected in many areas due to deep habitat.

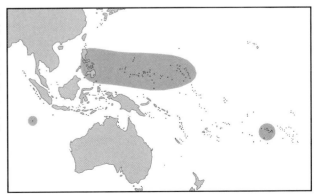

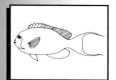

Genicanthus caudovittatus
Zebra Angelfish
(Günther 1860)

Female

Roger Steene

Male

Roger Steene

Habitat Seaward reef slopes with abundant coral growth, between 15-70 m.

Characters Male: White with numerous thin black bars on head and sides; spinous dorsal fin with yellow margin and distinctive black marking, lacking in the similar *Genicanthus melanospilos* (opposite) from the western Pacific. Female: White with black caudal lobes; black bar above eye (lacking in the similar *G. melanospilos* female). Maximum size about 20 cm.

Remarks Males occur either solitary or in small groups (usually a single male with several smaller females). Females usually in small aggregations. Often seen swimming well above the bottom feeding on zooplankton. Capable of sex reversal, internal sex change takes place before external color change.

Distribution Western Indian Ocean along the East African coast, from Mozambique northwards to the Red Sea (common in the Gulf of Aqaba), also at Mauritius.

Genicanthus melanospilos
Black-Spot Angelfish
(Bleeker 1857)

Roger Streene

Male

Female

Gerald R. Allen

Habitat   Outer reef slopes among coral or in rubble areas, often interspersed with sandy bottoms between 20-45 m. Frequently seen at base of outer reef drop-offs.

Characters   Male: Bluish-white with narrow black bars on sides and upper part of head; faint yellow spots on dorsal, caudal and anal fins; tail base yellowish; black spot on breast. Female: Upper half of body and dorsal fin yellow, grading to pale blue below; caudal fin bluish with black markings on upper and lower edges. Closely related to and similar in appearance to *Genicanthus caudovittatus* (opposite) from the Red Sea and western Indian Ocean. Males of *G. melanospilos* are distinguished by the lack of a black marking on the dorsal fin, and females by the lack of a black bar above the eye. Reaches maximum size of 18 cm.

Remarks   Usually occurs in pairs or small aggregations of one male with several females. Feeds on zooplankton up to a few meters above the bottom. Scientific name means black (*melano-*) spot (*-spilos*) and refers to the characteristic breast marking of males. The female was previously described as a separate species, *G. macclesfieldiensis*.

Distribution   Western Pacific Ocean, from Malaysia through the Indo-Australian Archipelago (including Rowley Shoals, Western Australia) to Fiji. Northwards to the Ryukyu Islands, and south to New Caledonia.

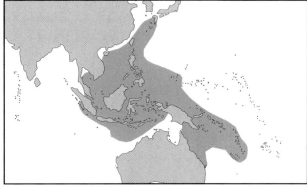

Genicanthus semicinctus
Half-Banded Angelfish
(Waite 1900)

Gerald R. Allen

Male

Female

Roger Steene

Habitat	Outer reef slopes below 10 m, but more abundant below 35 m.
Characters	Male: Bluish-white with series of (usually) 10 narrow black bars extending to middle of sides; dorsal fin, belly, caudal lobes and upper part of head faint yellow; black spots on caudal fin and rear edge of dorsal fin. Female: Head and upper half of body brown; lower body parts and fins white; caudal lobes with dark markings, rest of fin white; blue patch between eyes; ocellus directly above eye. Male similar to that of *Genicanthus spinus* (opposite) from the South Pacific, which attains larger size and lacks pronounced spotting on the tail.
Remarks	The original description was based on male specimens. Females were not discovered until 1973 at Lord Howe Island. Relatively common on deep rocky reefs at Lord Howe.
Distribution	Known only from Lord Howe and the Kermadec Island in the southwestern Pacific Ocean.

Genicanthus spinus
Pitcairn Angelfish
Randall 1975

Male

John E. Randall

Female

John E. Randall

Habitat Outer reef slopes, at depths ranging from 30 to at least 60 m.

Characters Male: Pale bluish-white overall with about 11 narrow black bars on upper half of body to caudal-fin base; pale gray markings on most of head and breast; very faint yellow markings on dorsal and anal fins, also on caudal lobes; small black spot in middle of caudal fin; caudal fin ending in very elongate filaments. Similar to male of *Genicanthus semicinctus* (opposite), but lacking the prominent yellow coloration. Female: Uniformly pale blue-greenish white on upper half of body and on dorsal, anal and caudal fins; lower half of body and belly white. Attains 35 cm (including tail filaments).

Remarks Forms plankton-feeding aggregations that swim in mid-water. The diet is supplemented by benthic organisms.

Distribution Known from only a small number of localities in the South Pacific including the Austral Islands (Raivavae, Rurutu), the Pitcairn group (including Ducie Atoll) and Rarotonga in the Cook Islands.

Genicanthus lamarck
Lamarck's Angelfish
(Lacépède 1802)

Male

Roger Steene

Roger Steene

Female

Habitat Most often occurring on seaward reef slopes between 10-50 m, sometimes seen in more protected areas (e.g. near wharf at Samarai Island, Papua New Guinea).

Characters Male: White with three or four black stripes on side (width of stripes varies between individuals); black dorsal and pelvic fins; caudal fin with numerous faint black spots; yellow spot on nape. Female: Similar to male but smaller; white with three or four stripes (varying in width between individuals) on side, uppermost stripe broader than others; dorsal fin with broad black edge; pelvic fin white; caudal fin with faint black spots and black upper and lower edges. Attains maximum size of 23 cm.

Remarks Forms aggregations that swim well above the bottom, feeding on zooplankton.

Distribution Throughout the Indo-Australian Archipelago to Vanuatu. As far north as southern Japan, and southwards to the northern Great Barrier Reef.

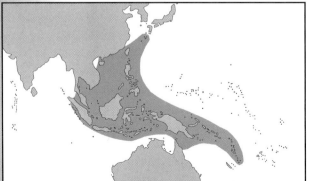

Genicanthus watanabei
Watanabe's Angelfish
(Yasuda & Tominaga 1970)

Male — Roger Steene

Female — Roger Steene

Habitat Steep seaward reefs and drop-offs, at depths between 12-81 m. Frequently in areas swept by strong currents.

Characters Male: Pale blue on head, upper part of body and caudal region; lower part of body with alternating black and white stripes; short yellow stripe anterior to caudal-fin base; dorsal and anal fins with broad black margin. Female: Pale bluish-white overall; black markings above eye and on forehead; dorsal and anal fins with black margin; black markings on caudal lobes. Maximum size about 15 cm.

Remarks Occurs in small or large mixed sex aggregations which swim in mid-water, high off the bottom. Planktonic items are the major dietary component, supplemented with benthic invertebrates. Spawning occurs shortly after sunset. Eggs measure 0.8 mm in diameter and hatch in about 16-18 hours.

Distribution Western and central Pacific, from Taiwan to the Tuamotu Archipelago. North to the Ryukyu Islands and south to New Caledonia and the Austral Islands. Rare in the Australia-New Guinea region.

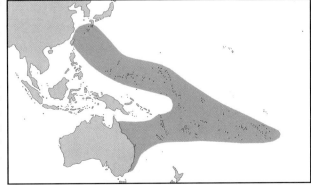

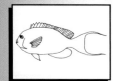

Genicanthus personatus
Masked Angelfish
Randall 1975

Male

Female

Habitat   Seaward reef slopes below 23 m depth.

Characters   Female: White, face usually dark; orange marking on pelvic fin; caudal fin black on anterior half and white posteriorly, without filaments. Male: Similar to female but with distinctive orange face and broad orange band on dorsal and anal fins; caudal fin similar to female but ending in short filaments. Maximum size about 21 cm.

Remarks   Female was first discovered in 1972 by aquarium fish collectors. First males were found three years later. Analyses of stomach contents reveal this species feeds on the green alga *Codium*, planktonic organisms, and fish eggs.

Distribution   Restricted to the Hawaiian Islands where it is more common in the northwestern islands.

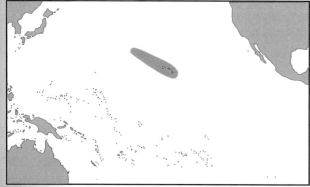

Genicanthus semifasciatus
Japanese Swallow
(Kamohara 1934)

John E. Randall

Female

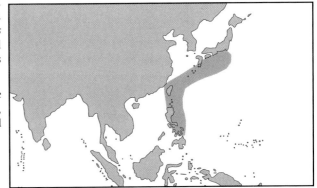

Male

John E. Randall

Habitat Rocky or coral reef areas on seaward slopes, from 15 to at least 100 m depth.

Characters Male: White overall with black bars on upper half of body; orange markings on face and gill cover, narrowing to a mid-lateral stripe; faint orange spots on dorsal and caudal fins. Female: Dusky brown on upper parts of body and dorsal fin, becoming white below; black markings above and behind eye and also on margin of gill cover with white coloration in between; black caudal-fin base and caudal lobes. Maximum size about 21 cm. Superficially similar to *G. semicinctus* (page 73) from Lord Howe Island and the Kermadecs, but both male and female easily distinguished on the basis of color pattern.

Remarks Mixed sex aggregations characteristic of other members of the genus are apparently uncommon in this species. Consequently, females were known as a separate species, *Holacanthus fuscosus*, for many years until color transformation was observed in an aquarium.

Distribution Western Pacific rim from the northern Philippines, Taiwan, Ryukyu and Izu Islands, and southern Japan.

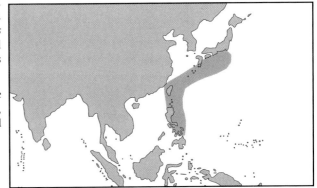

78

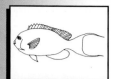

Genicanthus takeuchii
Spotted Angelfish
Pyle 1997

John E. Randall

Male

Female

John E. Randall

Habitat Outer reef slopes, usually below 36 m.

Characters Male: Bluish-white overall with numerous thin black stripes on upper half of body; dorsal and caudal fins white with numerous prominent black spots. Female: Bluish-white with detailed pattern of closely-spaced narrow black lines on upper parts of body and head, sometimes appearing as a checkered pattern; belly pale; fine black markings and spots on face and dorsal, anal and caudal fins; caudal lobes white. Reaches maximum size of about 25 cm.

Remarks This is the most recently described member of the family. Observed in haremic aggregations of one male and several females. Has been recorded from areas of cool, upwelling (20°C).

Distribution Thus far known only from the Bonin Islands (Chichi-Jima) and Marcus Island in the northwestern Pacific Ocean.

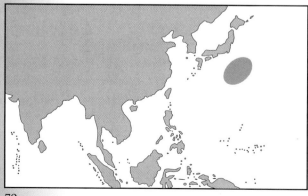

Paracentropyge venusta
Purple-Mask or Blue-Backed Angelfish
(Yasuda & Tominaga 1969)

John E. Randall

Habitat   Occupant of caves, usually on steep outer reef slopes, from 15-35 m.

Characters   Yellow ground color with two large blue patches - one covering upper rear half of body, extending on to dorsal and caudal fins, and other forming triangular blue patch from forehead to pectoral fin base; light blue markings on caudal and dorsal fins as well as margins of ventral fins. Attains 12 cm.

Remarks   A secretive species, usually observed singly, almost always upside down in reef caves. Apparently a close relative of *Paracentropyge multifasciata* (page 81) with which it hybridizes in the wild.

Distribution   Western Pacific rim, from north Luzon in the Philippines to Taiwan. Also at the Ryukyus (particularly common at Kerama Island) and Izu Islands.

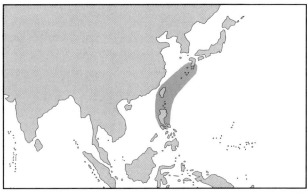

Paracentropyge multifasciata
Multi-Barred Angelfish
(Smith & Radcliffe 1911)

★ ★

Roger Steene

Habitat Generally in crevices and caves on steep outer reef slopes and drop-offs, between 20-70 m. Occasionally observed on shallower lagoon reefs.

Characters White with series of about eight brown bars on head and sides, becoming yellow ventrally; mouth and pelvic fin yellow; caudal fin white with a number of solid or broken brown bars. Juveniles with brown spot on rear corner of dorsal fin. Maximum size about 10 cm.

Remarks Occurs singly or in small aggregations. Sightings of small groups swimming upside down on the roof of large caves on the outer reef are not uncommon. A very shy species which quickly retreats to shelter when encountered by divers.

Distribution Cocos-Keeling Island to the Society Islands, north to the Ryukyu Islands and south to the Great Barrier Reef.

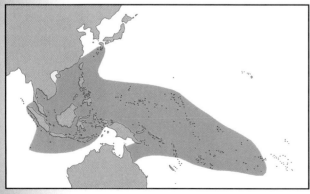

Paracentropyge boylei
Peppermint Angelfish
(Pyle & Randall 1992)

Richard Pyle

Habitat Coral rubble areas on steep outer reef slopes, between 56-120 m.

Characters Series of five alternating broad red-orange and narrower white bars on side; bars extend onto adjacent fins (pelvic, dorsal and anal); rear edge of dorsal and anal fins blue; head orange above, becoming more yellow below; caudal fin yellowish, slightly transparent. Juvenile similar to adult, but has four evenly-spaced white bars rather than five. Maximum size of 7 cm.

Remarks Found singly, or in small aggregations of 4-6 individuals (presumably harem groups). A secretive species, usually dwelling within cracks and crevices, or under ledges among rubble. Has been observed picking at rubble, probably feeding on benthic invertebrates. At depth, red bars appear blackish. First collected in depths of around 100 m using conventional scuba. After surfacing the collectors could not recall collecting the fish only minutes before, so severe were the effects of nitrogen narcosis.

Distribution Known only from Rarotonga near the Cook Islands in the South Pacific. Further exploration of deep water in the future will probably result in expansion of its range.

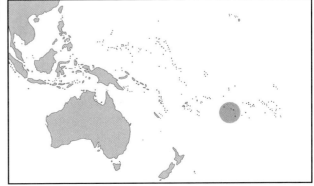

Pomacanthus asfur
Arabian or Crescent Angelfish
(Forsskål 1775)

Gerald R. Allen

Habitat   Protected shoreline reefs with rich growth of hard and soft corals mixed with silt bottoms, in relatively shallow water between 3-15 m. Visibility in these areas is frequently reduced.

Characters   Adult: Dark overall with broad, vertical yellow marking at middle of body, tapering to a point ventrally; scales on front part of body dark iridescent blue; head black; caudal fin yellow; dorsal and anal fins ending in filaments. Juvenile: Bluish-black ground with series of narrow white and pale blue bars on sides, usually three bars prominently white; slightly larger juveniles with yellow marking dorsally and yellow caudal fin distinguishes them from similar juveniles of *Pomacanthus maculosus* (opposite). Reaches maximum size of 40 cm.

Remarks   A solitary, relatively shy species, not easy to approach. Usually observed near large crevices or caves on the reef, seldom venturing away from these refuges. Feeds mainly on sponges and tunicates.

Distribution   Western Indian Ocean, from the Red Sea and Gulf of Aden, south to Zanzibar.

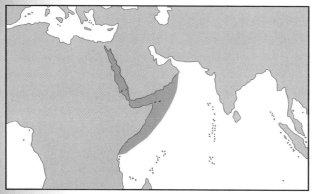

Pomacanthus maculosus
Yellow-Band Angelfish
(Forsskål 1775)

Juvenile

Adult

Habitat Coral-rich reefs and protected silty bays with coral and wreckage debris, between 4-12 m.

Characters Adult: Unusual violet-blue with large yellow blotch on middle of body; scales on forehead and nape with darker edges; yellowish patch on dorsal fin with light blue markings, same pattern on caudal fin; dorsal and anal fins ending in filaments. Juvenile: Dark ground color with numerous closely spaced pale blue and white bars on sides; caudal fin transparent, distinguishing it from similar juvenile of *Pomacanthus asfur* (opposite), which has yellow caudal fin. Maximum size of 50 cm.

Remarks A curious fish which closely approaches divers, making an ideal photographic subject. Often retreats to shelter after initial curiosity. Usually encountered singly. Yellow marking on sides appears on juveniles at size of about 6 cm, full transformation to adult coloration occurs at 10-15 cm. Hybridizes with *Pomacanthus chrysurus* (page 85). Sold at fish markets of Bahrain and Qatar.

Distribution Around the Arabian Peninsula including the Red Sea (Eilat, Jeddah), Gulf of Oman (common near Muscat) and the Arabian Gulf. Southwards to Kenya on the East African coast.

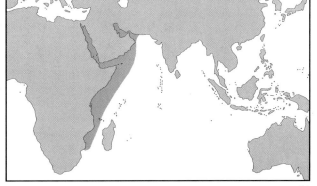

84

Pomacanthus chrysurus
Ear-Spot Angelfish
(Cuvier 1831)

★ ★

Gerald R. Allen

Habitat Shallow reefs with rich coral growth, between 1-25 m.

Characters Adult: Dark brown overall with six narrow white bars from dorsal fin to below middle of sides; blue lines on face and gill cover; orange-rimmed dark spot above gill cover; pelvic and anal fins orange with blue stripes; caudal fin yellow with blue rear margin. Juvenile: Dark ground color with unique widely-spaced narrow white and pale blue bars on side; caudal fin yellow with white bar in middle. Maximum size approximately 33 cm.

Remarks An uncommon species, probably most abundant along the Kenyan coast. Hybrids between this species and *Pomacanthus maculosus* (page 84) have been recorded.

Distribution Western Indian Ocean from Gulf of Aden to Natal (South Africa). Also at Seychelles, Comoros and Madagascar.

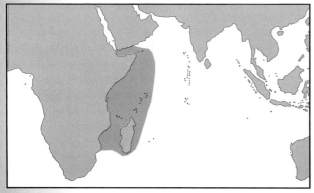

Pomacanthus imperator
Emperor Angelfish
(Bloch 1787)

Roger Steene

Adult

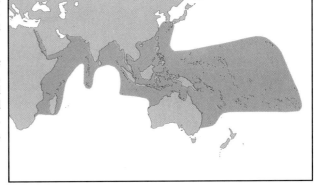

Roger Steene

Juvenile

Habitat Coastal and outer reefs, also deep lagoons, often in areas of rich coral growth between 6-60 m. Commonly seen near ledges and caves. Juveniles usually occur under ledges or in holes on shallow reefs.

Characters Adult: Vivid pattern of alternating diagonal narrow yellow and broader blue stripes; greenish yellow marking with blue margin on forehead extending behind eye to cheek spine; dark eye mask and broad dark bar behind head, merging with breast region; whitish snout and cheek; yellow-orange caudal fin. Juvenile: Dark blue-black with unique pattern of white concentric circular markings on body. Adult coloration apparent at about 8-12 cm length. Maximum size about 38 cm.

Remarks Adults occurring solitary or paired, juveniles usually solitary. Soft dorsal fin sometimes forming short filament (rounded in Indian Ocean specimens). When disturbed, emits a peculiar knocking sound.

Distribution Widespread throughout the Indo-west and central Pacific, from East Africa and the Red Sea to the Tuamotu, Line and Hawaiian Islands (rare). South to New Caledonia, north to southern Japan.

86

Pomacanthus navarchus
Blue-Girdled Angelfish
(Cuvier 1831)

Roger Steene

Habitat   Areas of rich coral growth in lagoons, channels and on outer reef slopes, from 3-40 m. Juveniles mostly in shallow protected reef areas.

Characters   Adult: Largely yellow-orange including dorsal and caudal fins, scale centers blue; deep blue marking with bright blue margins from forehead, narrowing to belly, along ventral surface to rear part of body and anal fin; prominent deep blue filamentous pelvic fins with neon blue anterior edge. Juvenile: Series of narrow vertical blue bars on; unusually large pelvic fins; orange tinge to dorsal fin; transparent caudal fin. Adult coloration assumed at 3-8 cm. Attains 25 cm.

Remarks   Usually encountered singly. Relatively timid, but can usually be approached at close range, if only momentarily. Diet comprised mostly of sponges and tunicates. Hybridizes with *Pomacanthus xanthometopon* (page 92).

Distribution   Throughout Indo-Australian Archipelago and western edge of Micronesia, including Rowley Shoals (off Western Australia), northwards to Philippines, Palau and Yap. Relatively common at many locations in Indonesia.

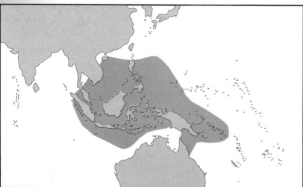

Pomacanthus rhomboides
Old Woman Angelfish
(Rüppell 1835)

Adll

Gerald R. Allen

Adult

Gerald R. Allen

Juvenile

Habitat Coastal coral reefs and rocky shoreline areas from 5-30 m. Juveniles occupy shallow tide pools.

Characters Adult: Very deep bodied with hump on forehead; gray overall with large triangular pale blue patch on rear portion of body; yellowish on ventral part of body below pelvic fins. Juvenile: Very similar to juvenile *Pomacanthus annularis* (page 91), with dark ground color and pale blue and white bars on side; transparent caudal fin sometimes with faint darker markings, distinguishes it from juvenile of *P. annularis*. Attains 46 cm.

Remarks Unique member of the genus both in terms of its appearance (i.e. deep body, drab coloration) and behavior. Small groups of adults occasionally seen swimming above reefs in midwater, sometimes close to the surface feeding on plankton. Apparently the flesh is good eating.

Distribution East Africa from southern Red Sea to South Africa (Knysna). Also at Madagascar.

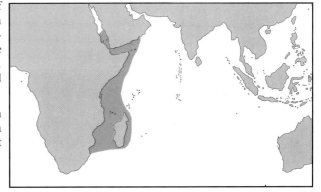

Pomacanthus semicirculatus
Semicircle Angelfish
(Cuvier 1831)

Sub-Adult

Juvenile

Adult

Habitat Protected coastal reefs with rich coral growth, from 1-40 m. Adults sometimes seen in caves and on wrecks. Juveniles prefer shallow reefs mixed with sand bottoms.

Characters Adult: Dusky brownish green on anterior and posterior sections of body; middle of body paler yellow-green; blue margins on all fins except pectorals; blue markings on cheek and gill cover; cheek spine blue; mouth pale yellow; dorsal and anal fins ending in short filaments. Juvenile: Distinctive semicircular narrow blue and white lines on rear half of body becoming more vertical anteriorly; caudal fin dark with white bars and white margin. Color transformation from juvenile to adult takes place at 8-16 cm. Maximum size about 35 cm.

Remarks Generally solitary in habit. Juveniles shy and cryptic when very small. Food items include sponges, tunicates and algae.

Distribution Widely dispersed throughout the Indo-west Pacific, from East Africa to Fiji. Northern extremity of range is southern Japan, southern extremity is northwest and eastern Australia (NSW, Lord Howe Island). Common at Seychelles and tropical western Pacific.

Pomacanthus sexstriatus
Six-Banded Angelfish
(Cuvier 1831)

Adult

Gerald R. Allen

Roger Steene

Juvenile

Habitat Coastal, lagoon and outer reef slopes in clear or murky water between 3-60 m. Shows a preference for coral-rich areas, especially on steep reef walls. Juveniles more common on shallower protected reefs.

Characters Adult: Tan with blue scale centers and five broad dark bars on sides; dark head with white bar behind eye; vivid blue spots on caudal fin and rear edge of anal and dorsal fins. Juvenile: Five prominent white bars on body (slightly curved backwards at extremities) and a sixth behind eye with inconspicuous blue lines between; fins with blue margins. Juveniles begin color transformation at 8-15 cm. Reaches maximum size of 46 cm. Juvenile similar to *Pomacanthus xanthometopon* (page 92) but corners of dorsal and anal fins slightly elevated giving a more angular appearance.

Remarks One of the largest angelfish species. Occurring solitary or in pairs, adults are shy and usually seek shelter if closely approached. When distressed they emit a grunting sound. Hybridizes in the wild with *P. xanthometopon*.

Distribution Throughout the Indo-Australian Archipelago and western Pacific rim. East to the Solomon Islands, north as far as the Ryukyu Islands and southwards to New Caledonia and Rowley Shoals (Western Australia).

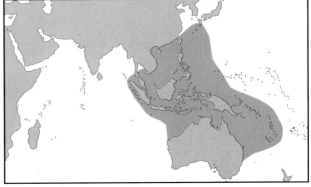

Pomacanthus annularis

Blue-Ringed Angelfish

(Bloch 1787)

★★

Roger Steene

Adult

Juvenile

Roger Steene

Habitat Coastal reefs at depths between 1-60 m. Sometimes encountered in caves, on wrecks, or underneath jetties in sheltered coves or harbors. Frequently seen in murky water.

Characters Adult: Brown overall with curved blue lines on body and soft portions of dorsal and anal fins; blue ring above gill cover; caudal fin white with yellow margin. Juvenile: Bars on sides slightly curve backwards at extremities; 3 or 4 prominent white bars (2-3 on body, 1 behind eye), remainder of bars light blue; caudal fin tinged white; frequently with blue circular markings on soft dorsal fin. Maximum size attained 45 cm. Juveniles similar to those of *Pomacanthus rhomboides* (page 88) and *P. maculosus* (page 84); all co-occur on the eastern African coast.

Remarks Usually encountered singly or in pairs. Feeds on zooplankton, sponges, and tunicates. Tip of dorsal fin sometimes elongate, forming a short filament.

Distribution Wide ranging throughout the Indo-west Pacific region. Rare at East Africa (north of Natal) and Madagascar, more common at Sri Lanka. Occurs throughout Indonesia eastwards to New Guinea and the Solomon Islands. Northwards to southern Japan.

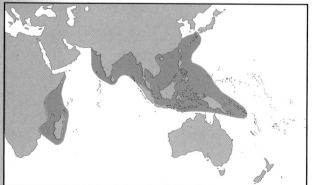

Pomacanthus xanthometopon
Yellow-Mask or Blue-Face Angelfish
(Bleeker 1853)

Roger Steene

Habitat   Areas of prolific coral growth in lagoons, channels and on outer reef slopes between 5-30 m. Especially in areas with caves and large crevices.

Characters   Adult: Body scales blue with bright yellow edges, giving reticulated appearance, becoming whitish on dorsal fin; golden breast and pectoral region; blue head with black markings on snout and golden spots on cheek; yellow eye mask; yellow on caudal and rear portion of dorsal fin; dark spot on rear of dorsal fin. Juvenile: Six prominent white bars (curved backwards at extremities) with smaller, less conspicuous whitish-blue lines between; blue margin around body; tail dark with bluish bars. Juveniles assume adult color at 7-12 cm. Maximum size about 38 cm. Juveniles resemble those of *P. sexstriatus* (page 90), but white bars aren't as broad or prominent, and the dorsal and anal fins are more rounded..

Remarks   Solitary species which feeds on sponges and tunicates. Like most other members of the genus it makes grunting noise when distressed. Hybridizes with both *P. sexstriatus* and P. *navarchus*.

Distribution   Indo-west Pacific region, from the Maldives, through the Indo-Australian Archipelago to Vanuatu. Northwards through Carolines to Ryukyu Islands, and south to the Great Barrier Reef.

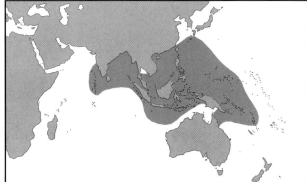

Pygoplites diacanthus
Regal Angelfish
(Boddaert 1772)

Roger Steene

Habitat Areas of rich coral growth in lagoons and on outer reefs, at depths between 1-48 m. Juveniles cryptic, remaining well hidden in cracks and crevices.

Characters Adult: Alternating yellow and dark-edged bluish-white bars on sides; soft portion of dorsal fin black, speckled blue; anal fin orange with blue stripes; caudal fin uniformly yellow. Juvenile: Similar pattern to adult but more orange-yellow overall with series of dark-edged white bars on sides; distinctive white-edged black ocellus on soft dorsal fin. Reaches maximum size of 25 cm.

Remarks Encountered singly, in pairs or uncommonly in small groups. A cautious species, always on the move between crevices. Feeds on sponges and tunicates. Aberrant color forms sometimes occur in nature. Indian Ocean populations have yellow breast distinguishing them from gray-breasted Pacific Ocean fish.

Distribution Widely distributed throughout the Indo-west and central Pacific, from the Red Sea to the Tuamotu Archipelago. Northwards to the Ryukyu Islands and south to New Caledonia.

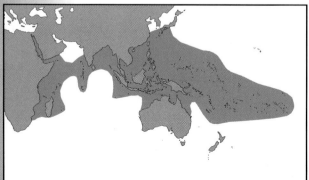

Amphichaetodon howensis
Lord Howe Butterflyfish
(Waite 1903)

Roger Steene

Habitat   Rocky reefs with some live coral growth in depths between 10-50 m.

Characters   Pale yellowish ground color becoming silver ventrally and on head; five black bars on side (three broad bars on body, one narrower bar through eye, a fifth at base of caudal fin); black stripe on snout; pelvic fins mostly black. Maximum size 18 cm. Resembles *Amphichaetodon melbae* (page 214) from the Eastern Pacific, but that species has much narrower black bars on the body.

Remarks   Diet comprised of small invertebrates. A relatively easy fish to approach which is most often encountered in moderately deep water, rarely in shallows. The only butterflyfish recorded from New Zealand.

Distribution   Southwest Pacific Ocean off the coast of southern Queensland and northern New South Wales (Australia), also at Lord Howe, Norfolk and Kermadec islands and northern New Zealand.

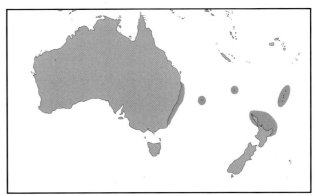

Chaetodon decussatus
Indian Vagabond Butterflyfish
Cuvier 1831

Roger Steene

Habitat Rubble or coral-rich areas from 1-30 m. Particularly common in turbid water.

Characters Mostly white with diagonal lines forming chevron-like markings on sides; posterior-most portion of body black; black bar through eye; caudal fin mostly yellow, with two black bars and a transparent margin. Maximum size reached is 20 cm. Closely related and similar in appearance to *C. vagabundus* (opposite), distinguished by the broad black area posteriorly on the body and fins.

Remarks A relatively territorial species usually occurring alone or in pairs. Feeds primarily on algae and coral polyps.

Distribution Northern Indian Ocean from Oman to the Andaman Sea, Bali (Indonesia), and Ashmore Reef in the Timor Sea. Also found at the Maldives, and is the most common butterflyfish on Sri Lankan reefs.

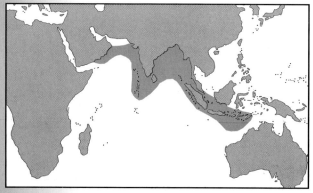

Chaetodon vagabundus
Vagabond Butterflyfish
Linnaeus 1758

Juvenile

Roger Steene

Roger Steene

Adult

Habitat Coral reef areas, from inner coastal reef flats to outer seaward slopes. Ranges in depth to 30 m.

Characters White with chevron-like markings on side; broad black band along rear edge of body; soft portions of dorsal and anal fins yellow; caudal fin yellow with central black bar; black bar through eye and horizontal yellow markings on snout. Juveniles similar to adult but with black spot on the soft dorsal fin. Reaches maximum size of 23 cm. Closely resembles *Chaetodon decussatus* (opposite), which differs in having considerable dark pigmentation the soft portion of the dorsal and anal fins.

Remarks Occurs singly, paired, or in small groups. Diet consists of anemones, coral polyps, polychaete worms and algae. Tolerates wide range of ecological conditions including turbid water and influxes of freshwater near river mouths.

Distribution Very widespread throughout the Indo-west and central Pacific, from coastal East Africa to Polynesia (Line Is., Tuamotus). Japan is the northern limit of the range and Lord Howe Island the southern.

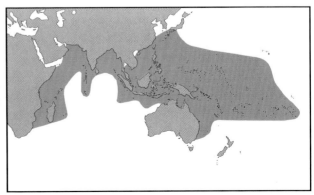

Chaetodon auriga
Threadfin Butterflyfish
Forsskål 1775

★ ★ ★

Roger Steene

Red Sea colour form

Roger Steene

Indo-Pacific colour form

Habitat Coastal, lagoonal and outer reefs. Most common in areas of rich coral growth on reef flats, and also in areas of mixed sand, coral and rubble. From 1-40 m depth.

Characters White ground color with chevron pattern of diagonal bands on the sides; posterior section of body yellow, with an adjacent dark patch; black bar through eye; black spot on soft dorsal fin which usually ends in a filament. The Red Sea population lacks the black spot on the dorsal fin. Maximum size to 23 cm. Chevron-like pattern is also seen in *C. vagabundus* (page 96) and *C. decussatus* (page 95), however these species have a dark bar on the rear part of the body.

Remarks Usually common throughout its distribution. Individuals cover large areas of the reef in search of food items including coral polyps, small crustaceans, polychaetes, anemones and algae. May form small aggregations, but is usually found alone or in pairs.

Distribution Wide ranging throughout the Indo-west and central Pacific from the Red Sea to the Hawaiian, Marquesas Islands, and Ducie Atoll. North as far as southern Japan and south to Lord Howe and Rapa Island. Vagrants occasionally seen in the eastern Pacific at the Galapagos.

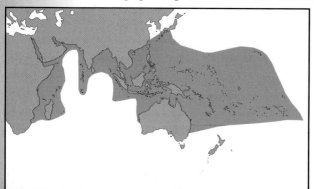

Chaetodon octofasciatus
Eight-Banded Butterflyfish
Bloch 1787

Roger Steene

Yellow form

Pale form

Roger Steene

Habitat Shallow, protected lagoons (often turbid and silty) and inner reefs with extensive coral growth, from 3-20 m.

Characters Body and fins bright yellow or mainly white, with series of eight black vertical bars, first one through eye, final one along rear edge of dorsal fin, through caudal fin base to anal fin; additional black stripe on snout; outer section of caudal fin transparent. Juveniles smaller than 5 cm usually have a cream ground color. Maximum size approximately 12 cm. Regional color variation is common. Fish from some areas (Palau and New Guinea) are mainly yellow, whereas those from Indonesia, Philippines and other parts of SE Asia are mainly white.

Remarks Adults usually found alone or in pairs, occasionally in small groups. Juveniles shelter amongst branching corals (*Acropora*). Diet consists exclusively of coral polyps. A common shoreline species able to tolerate reduced salinity.

Distribution Indo-west Pacific, from Sri Lanka to the Solomon Islands. North to the Ryukyu Islands, south to the Great Barrier Reef (rare).

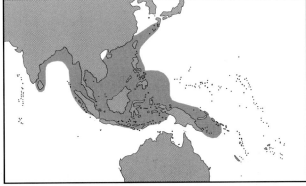

Chaetodon assarius
West Australian Butterflyfish
Waite 1905

Roger Steene

Habitat Coastal reefs in shallow water (less than 1 m) to at least 40 m depth.

Characters Silvery-tan body with five dark, broken vertical lines on upper part of sides; black bar through eye; silver-edged ocellus on soft dorsal fin; dark marking extending through anal fin and across base of tail, anterior margin of marking silver. Maximum size 13 cm.

Remarks Forms aggregations, sometimes containing numerous individuals. Preferred food items include algae and zooplankton. A close relative of *Chaetodon guentheri* (page 102) from southeastern Australia, and *C. dolosus* (page 101) from the western Indian Ocean.

Distribution Subtropical and temperate waters of the Western Australian coast from Perth to Shark Bay. Records of this species from cold upwelling areas at Bali (Indonesia) are possibly incorrectly identified specimens of *C. guentheri*.

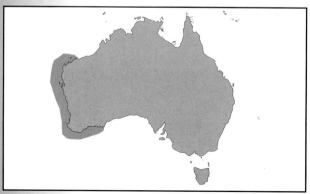

Chaetodon miliaris
Lemon Butterflyfish
Quoy & Gaimard 1824

Gerald R. Allen

Habitat Coastal fringing reefs, lagoons, and outer reefs, to at least 250 m. Juveniles found on shallow inner reefs from April to June.

Characters Yellow overall (aquarium specimens sometimes paler) with many dark spots on the side forming vertical lines; prominent black blotch on caudal-fin base; black bar through eye; all fins yellow. Maximum size about 13 cm. Frequently confused with similar-marked species including *C. assarius* (opposite), *C. guentheri* (page 102), C. dolosus (page 101), and *C. citrinellus* (page 147), however none of these have a black spot on the caudal-fin base.

Remarks Spawning occurs between December and April, but activity peaks in late February. Growth is rapid with onset of maturity (about 10 cm length) by the end of the first year. Occurs singly, paired, or in massive shoals of up to several hundred individuals, which sometimes swarm around SCUBA divers. Feeds in mid-water on zooplankton, supplementing the diet with benthic invertebrates and fish eggs (particularly those of damselfishes). Aggregations of *C. miliaris* , protected by sheer weight of numbers, commonly raid damselfish nests for eggs.

Distribution Restricted to the Hawaiian Islands (very abundant) and Johnston Atoll (much less common).

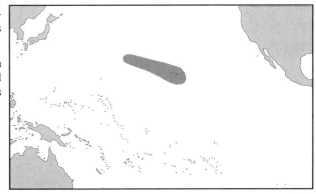

Chaetodon dolosus
African Butterflyfish
Ahl 1923

Habitat Deep offshore reefs with rocky or coral rubble substrates, from 40-200 m. Juveniles may occur on coral reefs as shallow as 8 m.

Characters Mostly whitish with numerous faint spots; black bar through eye; rear part of body dark brown to black becoming yellowish anteriorly (black region sometimes suffused with yellow, with a dark spot on the soft dorsal fin); caudal fin yellow; rear edge of dorsal and anal fins narrowly white. Maximum size about 14 cm. Bears a resemblance to *Chaetodon guentheri* (opposite) but is darker on the rear part of the body.

Remarks Solitary or paired. Occasionally observed with *Chaetodon mitratus* (page 130). Most specimens have been collected with trawls operating in relatively deep water.

Distribution East African coast from Somalia to Natal, also at Mauritius (and probably Madagascar).

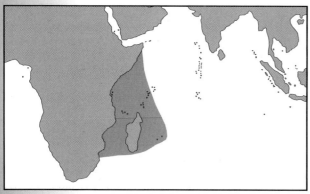

Chaetodon guentheri
Günther's Butterflyfish
Ahl 1913

Habitat Rocky reefs as well as coral-rich outer slopes from 5 to at least 40 m.

Characters Body mostly whitish or creamy yellow with faint spotting; posterior-most part of body and adjacent fins yellow; black bar through eye. Grows to a maximum of 14 cm. Closely resembles *C. dolsosus* (opposite), *C. assarius* (page 99), and *C. miliaris* (page 100), but these species have dark pigmentation at the rear of the body, lacking in *C. guentheri*.

Remarks In tropical areas it frequents slopes adjacent to deep water exposed to cool upwellings (e.g. Bali, Komodo, N. Sulawesi). Probably more common in the subtropical and temperate portion of its range.

Distribution Western Pacific Ocean including Lord Howe Island, coastal New South Wales, the Great Barrier Reef, southern Papua New Guinea, Indonesia (Komodo and northern Sulawesi), Taiwan, Ryukyu Islands and southern Japan.

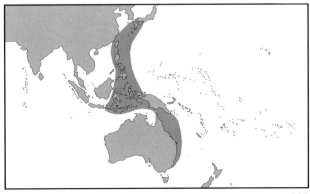

Chaetodon aureofasciatus
Golden-Striped Butterflyfish
Macleay 1878

Roger Steene

Habitat Coastal and inner reefs in relatively shallow water, 5-15 m. Juveniles frequently among branching corals.

Characters Nearly circular body, snout not prominently projected; body yellow overall with large dusky grayish patch; dark-edged golden-orange bar through eye; caudal fin yellow with transparent rear edge. Juvenile similar to adult. Reaches a maximum size of 12.5 cm. *Chaetodon rainfordi* (opposite) is similar in appearance, but has cross bands on the body.

Remarks Occurs either solitary or paired. Feeds predominantly on coral polyps and algae on shallow reefs. Able to tolerate high proportions of fresh water in its natural habitat, consequently is commonly seen on coastal reefs near river mouths. Hybrids of this species and *C. rainfordi* have been recorded from the wild.

Distribution Tropical Australian coast from northwestern Australia to the Great Barrier Reef and northern New South Wales, also southern New Guinea.

Chaetodon rainfordi
Rainford's Butterflyfish
McCulloch 1923

Roger Steene

Habitat Coastal and offshore reefs in areas of sparse coral growth, to 15 m depth.

Characters Adult: Yellow with two broad bluish-gray bars (containing small dark spots) with yellow-orange margins on body; a third narrower orange bar edged anteriorly with grayish blue through pectoral region; dark edged orange bar through eye and dark snout stripe present; dark streak on tail base. Juvenile: Paler with more prominent dusky bars; eye-bar is black above; circular ocellus on tail base. Maximum size about 15 cm. Similar to *Chaetodon aureofasciatus* (opposite), which lacks bars on body.

Remarks Occurs either singly or in pairs. Feeds predominantly on algae, supplemented with small benthic invertebrates. Easy to approach underwater.

Distribution Restricted to coastal Queensland, the neighboring Great Barrier Reef, Lord Howe Island, and parts of southern Papua New Guinea.

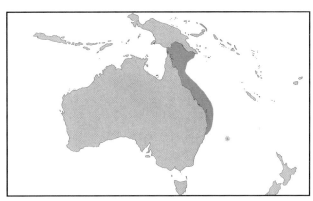

Chaetodon auripes
Oriental Butterflyfish
Jordan & Snyder 1901

Roger Steene

Habitat Rocky reefs with some growth of coral and algae. Juveniles occupy tide pools and shallow, protected rocky areas. Depth range 1-30 m.

Characters Adult: Ground color light to dusky golden with numerous narrow, darkened horizontal stripes; black bar through eye with prominent white bar immediately behind; snout tip black; fins at rear of body with narrow dark margin. Juvenile: Similar to adult, but with ocellus on dorsal fin and clear caudal fin. Maximum size about 20 cm. Sometimes confused with *Chaetodon collare* (page 135), but that species is much darker and its tail is mainly red. Also resembles *C. wiebeli* (opposite), which differs in having slanted stripes and an angular bend in the white bar at the back of the head.

Remarks Forms aggregations but is commonly seen alone. Feeds mostly on small benthic invertebrates. Can survive in temperatures as low as 10°C in Japan.

Distribution Western Pacific rim from South China Sea, including Taiwan, to southern Japan (common at southern Honshu, Shikoku and Kyushu) and the Izu Islands.

Chaetodon wiebeli
Wiebel's Butterflyfish
Kaup 1863

Yohji Ohkata

Habitat Rocky reefs and coral areas, from 4 to at least 25 m.

Characters Adult: Golden with diagonal reddish-brown lines on sides; head with black markings (on snout tip, through eye, and from upper gill cover across nape) separated by white markings; caudal fin with broad black bar edged on either side in white. Juvenile: Similar to adult but posterior-most black head-marking extends to the lower part of the gill cover; soft dorsal fin with an ocellated spot, and; a black bar across caudal fin base. Grows to a maximum size of about 18 cm. *Chaetodon auripes* (opposite) is superficially similar, but lacks the black marking across the nape.

Remarks Usually occurs solitary, but also forms pairs. Grazes on algal-covered rocks, presumably supplementing this diet with other food items such as benthic invertebrates and coral polyps.

Distribution Eastern Asian coast along the extreme western Pacific rim, from the Gulf of Thailand north to southern Japan. Most common off the coast of China.

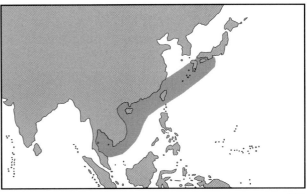

Chaetodon austriacus
Exquisite Butterflyfish
Rüppell 1835

Roger Steene

Habitat Lagoonal and fringing coral-rich reefs in clear water, to 20 m depth.

Characters Golden with narrow gray stripes on body, one widens to form dark streak on back; three dark bars on head; dorsal fin white; anal and caudal fins, and margin of soft dorsal fin black (distinguishes this species from the similar *C. trifasciatus* and *C. lunulatus*. Juvenile is more pale than adult and has a spot at the base of the caudal fin. Attains 13 cm. *C. melapterus* (opposite) is also very similar, but distinguished by its black dorsal fin.

Remarks Occurs solitary, in pairs or sometimes in small shoals. Diet is comprised mostly of live coral polyps, but gastropod eggs and anemones are also consumed. Juveniles inhabit a single coral head until they reach maturity.

Distribution Red Sea and adjacent Gulf of Aden, rarely to coast of Oman.

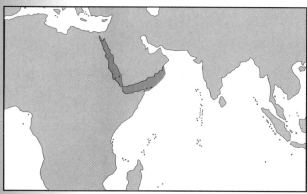

Chaetodon melapterus
Arabian Butterflyfish
Guichenot 1862

Gerald R. Allen

Habitat Coastal reefs rich in coral growth interspersed with sand patches, from 2-16 m.

Characters Adult: Orange-yellow with faint horizontal lines on side; dorsal, caudal and anal fins black with a narrow pale edge; mouth black; two black bars on head including one through eye separated by a gold bar. Juvenile: Orange-yellow overall with black bar through eye and darkened anal and caudal fins. Dorsal fin darkens with growth. Attains 12 cm. Adults are similar in appearance to *Chaetodon austriacus* (opposite), but differ in having a black dorsal fin.

Remarks Usually encountered in pairs, but sometimes observed in larger aggregations numbering in excess of 20 individuals. Feeds mainly on coral polyps but also consumes benthic invertebrates. Specific name translates to black (*mela-*) fin (*-pterus*).

Distribution Southern Red Sea to the Arabian Gulf.

Chaetodon lunulatus
Redfin Butterflyfish
Quoy & Gaimard, 1824

Roger Steene

Juvenile

Roger Steene

Adult

Habitat   Rich coral areas in lagoons and on seaward reefs to depths of about 20 m.

Characters   Pinkish, becoming yellow on head and ventral part of body; series of slightly oblique purple-blue stripes on sides; black bar through eye with golden margins and narrower dark vertical line behind eye; anal fin red with yellow-edged black band on base; similar dark band at base of soft dorsal fin and across middle of tail fin. Maximum size about 15 cm. Similar to *C. trifasciatus* (opposite) from the Indian Ocean, but lacks blue color on rear half of body and anal fin is darker red.

Remarks   Found in pairs or small groups. Diet consists solely of live corals. Occurs in monogamous pairs which defend a feeding territory. At Okinawa (Japan) spawning occurs at dusk during the time of full moon and new moon. Pairs migrate 100-400 m from the territory to the spawning site (where currents run towards to the open sea).

Distribution   Widespread in the western Pacific from eastern Australia northwards to Japan and eastwards to the Tuamotu Islands and Hawaii. Also occurs along the Western Australian coast. Occurs with sibling species *C. trifasciatus* on the Indonesian island of Bali.

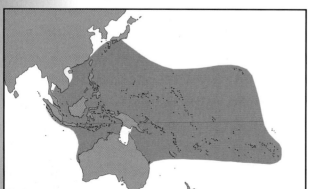

Chaetodon trifasciatus
Indian Ocean Redfin Butterflyfish
Park 1797

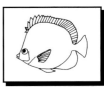

Roger Steene

Habitat   Coral rich, protected areas in lagoons and on seaward reefs, to 20 m.

Characters   Pale orange, becoming more yellowish ventrally, with series of slightly oblique purplish-blue stripes on sides; back and rear part of body with strong purple-blue tint; black bar through eye with golden edges, and vertical dark line behind eye; anal fin red-orange with yellow-edged black band at base; similar band at base of soft dorsal fin and centrally on caudal fin. Maximum size about 15 cm. Closely related to and once thought to be synonymous with *Chaetodon lunulatus* (opposite) from the western and central Pacific, which lacks the strong purple-blue color on the body and has dusky red, rather than bright orange red, caudal fin. Also related to *Chaetodon austriacus* (page 107) from the Red Sea and *C. melapterus* (page 108) of the Arabian Peninsula and western Indian Ocean., which are more yellow overall.

Remarks   Home ranging species, usually encountered in pairs roaming the reef, avoiding other individuals of the same species. Diet is comprised primarily of coral polyps. Males with a red anal spine (pink in females).

Distribution   Indian Ocean from coastal East Africa to Bali, Indonesia and Christmas Island.

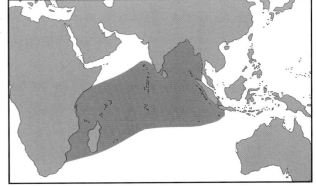

Chaetodon baronessa
Eastern Triangular Butterflyfish
Cuvier 1831

Roger Steene

Habitat Shallow lagoons and seaward reefs, usually in less than 10 m, among *Acropora* corals.

Characters Extremely deep-bodied, roughly triangular in shape; dark gray with many narrow, pale chevron markings on anterior two-thirds of body; head and breast region white with two dark bars, one through eye; mouth and snout black. Maximum size about 15 cm. Nearly identical to *Chaetodon triangulum* from the Indian Ocean (opposite), which differs in having a triangular black mark on the tail, rather than the narrow dark bar found in *C. baronessa*.

Remarks A territorial species, usually seen in pairs near *Acropora* corals. Feeds exclusively on the polyps of these corals. The narrow, compressed body allows this fish to retreat into crevices between the coral when threatened.

Distribution Widespread from Cocos-Keeling Atoll in the eastern Indian Ocean, through the Indo-Australian Archipelago to Fiji and Micronesia. Range extends north to southern Japan and south to northern New South Wales and New Caledonia.

Chaetodon triangulum
Triangular Butterflyfish
Cuvier 1831

Roger Steene

Habitat Coral reefs of lagoons and outer slopes where *Acropora* plate corals abound, from 3-15 m.

Characters Body shape roughly triangular; dark gray overall with many narrow, pale chevron markings on sides, more conspicuous on front part of body; head and breast paler with two dark reddish bars (one through eye); reddish mouth. Maximum size about 15 cm. Almost identical to *Chaetodon baronessa* from the western Pacific (opposite), which has a narrow black bar on the caudal fin instead of the more extensive diamond-shaped black patch characteristic of *C. triangulum*.

Remarks A territorial species, usually occurring in pairs, closely associated with *Acropora* plate corals. Feeds exclusively on the polyps of these corals. The Seribu Islands, near Jakarta off the Indonesian island of Java is the only locality where the closely related *C. triangulum* and *C. baronessa* are known to occur together.

Distribution Throughout the Indian Ocean, from Madagascar to Java and the Andaman Sea.

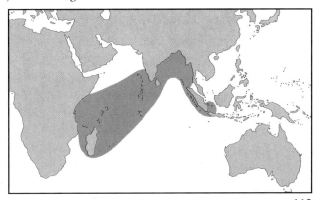

Chaetodon interruptus
Indian Ocean Teardrop Butterflyfish
Ahl 1923

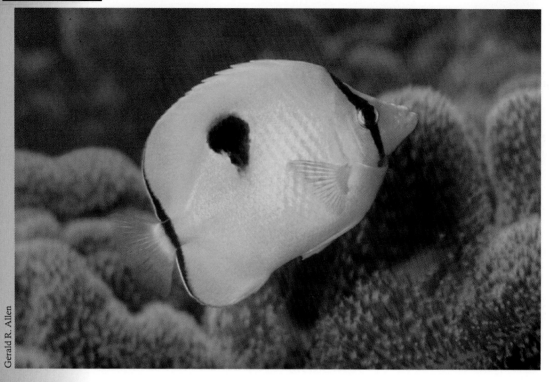

Gerald R. Allen

Habitat Lagoonal and seaward reefs, usually found in areas with abundant soft or hard corals. Depth ranges between about 10-40 m.

Characters Bright lemon yellow with black teardrop-shaped spot on upper side; black band along rear edge of body and fins and black bar through eye. Maximum size about 20 cm.

Remarks Occurs alone or in small groups. Feeds on a varied diet comprising hard and soft coral fragments, sponges, polychaetes, and filamentous algae. Similar to *C. unimaculatus* (opposite) from the western Pacific but differs in having bright yellow body. The two species were previously classified as subspecies of *C. unimaculatus* but the Indian Ocean and Pacific Ocean populations are geographically isolated and quite distinct in appearance.

Distribution Indian Ocean, from East Africa to the Andaman Sea.

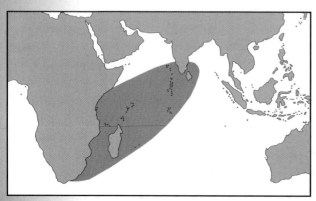

Chaetodon unimaculatus
Teardrop Butterflyfish
Bloch 1787

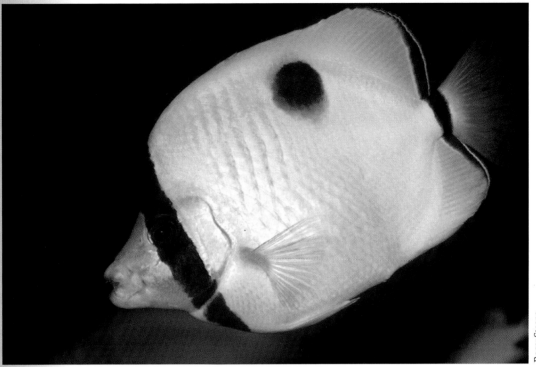

Roger Steene

Habitat Coral-rich reef flats, clear water lagoons and seaward reefs, to depths of 60 m. Particularly abundant where soft leather corals (*Sarcophyton* and *Sinularia* spp.) occur.

Characters White overall becoming yellow dorsally and on median fins; large black spot on upper sides; black band along rear edge of body and fins and black bar through eye. Maximum size about 20 cm.

Remarks Occurs in pairs and small aggregations. Feeds on a varied diet comprising hard and soft coral fragments, sponges, polychaetes, and filamentous algae. Large adults develop a bulbous snout. Similar to the closely related *C. interruptus* (opposite) from the Indian Ocean, but lacks yellow over most of the body. Hybrids between this species and *Chaetodon kleinii* (page XX) have been reported from Marshall Islands.

Distribution Western Pacific, from Indonesia to Polynesia (including Hawaiian Is, Marquesas, Ducie I, Rapa.). Northern limit of range is southern Japan, and extends south to Lord Howe Island. Also eastern Indian Ocean at northwestern Australia, Christmas Island, and Cocos-Keeling Islands.

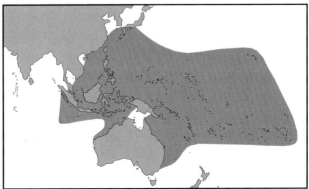

114

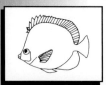

Chaetodon speculum
Oval-Spot Butterflyfish
Cuvier 1831

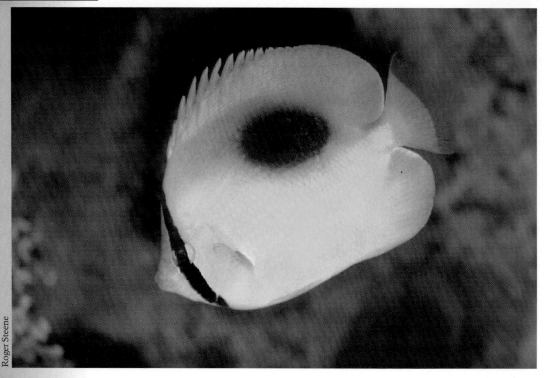

Roger Steene

Habitat   Coral-rich reefs of outer lagoons and seaward slopes, to a depth of 30 m.

Characters   Uniform yellow with large oval-shaped black spot on middle of upper sides; black bar through eye; caudal fin with transparent edge. Attains 18 cm. Similar to *Chaetodon zanzibariensis* (opposite), which has a smaller black spot and numerous thin lines on the sides .

Remarks   An uncommon and relatively shy species, usually encountered singly. Quickly retreats to shelter when approached at close range. Diet is comprised mostly of coral polyps and small benthic invertebrates.

Distribution   Ranges from Christmas Island in the Indian Ocean, eastward to Tonga in the Pacific. Northern extremity of range is southern Japan, south to Lord Howe Island off eastern Australia.

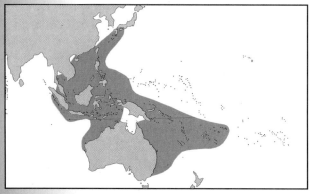

Chaetodon zanzibariensis
Zanzibar Butterflyfish
Playfair 1866

Roger Steene

Habitat Areas of rich coral growth in lagoons and on outer slopes, from 3-40 m. Abundant where staghorn corals (*Acropora*) occur.

Characters Golden yellow with series of faint stripes on the sides; large circular black spot on the upper sides; black bar through eye; caudal fin with transparent edge. Maximum size about 12 cm. Resembles *Chaetodon speculum* (opposite), which is more uniformly yellow (lacks faint striped pattern) and has a larger black spot on the side.

Remarks Occurs singly or in pairs. Also forms aggregations, particularly where staghorn coral is plentiful. Feeds primarily on coral polyps, but has also been observed feeding on coral spawn.

Distribution Western Indian Ocean, along the East African coast, south to Durban. Also at Mauritius and the Chagos Archipelago.

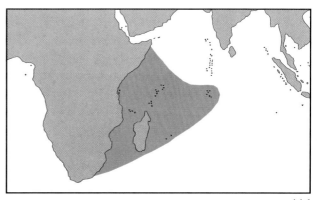

Chaetodon plebius
Blue-Spot Butterflyfish
Cuvier 1831

Juvenile

Roger Steene

Roger Steene

Adult

Habitat	Shallow environments including coastal, lagoon, and seaward reefs, to 10 m depth.
Characters	Yellow with faint dark horizontal lines and prominent light blue streak on side; light blue-edged black spot on tail base; light blue-edged black bar through eye to nape. Juveniles lack blue streak on side. Maximum size of about 15 cm.
Remarks	Occurring solitary, or often in pairs. Feeds mainly on coral polyps, juveniles have been observed cleaning ectoparasites from other fishes. Population from the Andaman Sea lacks the blue streak on the side and may eventually prove to be a separate species.
Distribution	Andaman Sea, throughout the Indo-Australian Archipelago to Fiji. Range extends north to southern Japan, south as far as Perth (Western Australia) and Lord Howe Island (off eastern Australia).

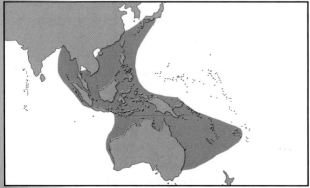

Chaetodon argentatus
Asian Butterflyfish
Smith & Radcliffe 1911

Roger Steene

Habitat	Rocky reef areas in the northern parts of the range, coral reef areas elsewhere. Ranges in depth between 5-20 m.
Characters	Pale overall with brown scale edges on body giving a reticulated pattern; broad brown to blackish marking across rear part of body and adjacent fins; two indistinct dusky brown patches on upper part of head and midbody; large fan-shaped caudal fin with central brown bar. Maximum size of about 20 cm.
Remarks	Generally encountered in pairs or small aggregations. Belongs to the *xanthurus* species complex containing *Chaetodon mertensii* (page 120), *C. xanthurus* (page 119), and *C. paucifasciatus* (page 121). The group is characterized by a network pattern on the body and a band of red, orange or dark brown posteriorly.
Distribution	Western Pacific rim including the Philippines, southern China, Taiwan, Ryukyu and Izu Islands, and southern Japan (common at Tanabe Bay directly south of Osaka on southern Honshu I.).

Chaetodon xanthurus
Yellow-Tail Butterflyfish
Bleeker 1857

Roger Steene

Habitat   Outer reef slopes and drop-offs among live coral, from 12-50 m.

Characters   White with black scale margins giving a crosshatched pattern on sides; posterior-most portion of body and adjacent fins orange; silver-edged black bar through eye and dark spot on nape; caudal fin white at base and orange on outer part. Reaches maximum size of approximately 14 cm.

Remarks   Occurs alone or in pairs, roaming widely across reefs in search of food (small benthic invertebrates and algae). Juveniles are shy, solitary, and restricted to confined areas close to shelter. Closely related to *Chaetodon mertensii* (opposite) from the Indo-west Pacific and *C. paucifasciatus* (page 121) from the Red Sea, which share a similar appearance. However, neither have the strong crosshatch pattern seen in this species.

Distribution   Western Pacific rim, from Indonesia and the Philippines to the Ryukyu Islands.

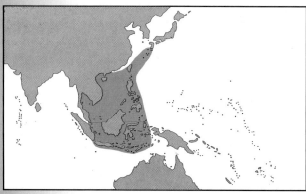

Chaetodon mertensii
Merten's Butterflyfish
Cuvier 1831

Habitat   Rocky or coral-covered reefs of lagoons and outer slopes (frequently seen adjacent to steep slopes and drop-offs), from 10-120 m. Sometimes observed around wharves and shipwrecks.

Characters   White with about 6-7 black chevron markings on side; broad yellow-orange band covering rear portion of body and adjacent fins; silver-edged black bar through eye continuous across forehead and dark smudge on nape (*madagaskariensis* variety which is illustrated has a discontinuous eye band and a silver-edged horseshoe shaped black mark on nape); caudal fin white at base, yellow-orange to edge. Attains 12.5 cm. Related to *C. xanthurus* (opposite), *C. paucifasciatus* (page 121), and *C. argentatus* (page 118). All have similar morphology but are readily distinguished on the basis of coloration

Remarks   *Chaetodon madagaskariensis* Ahl, formerly recognized as a distinct Indian Ocean species is now regarded as a colour variant of *C. mertensii*. Juveniles form aggregations, adults occur solitary or paired. Feeds on algae and benthic invertebrates.

Distribution   Ranges widely in the Indo-west Pacific East Africa to the Tuamotus, north to the Ryukyu Islands and south to Lord Howe and Rapa Island.

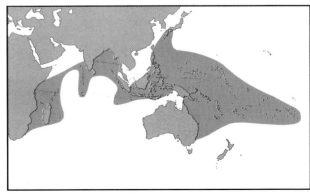

Chaetodon paucifasciatus
Red-Back or Crown Butterflyfish
Ahl 1923

★ ★ ★

Roger Steene

Habitat   Rubble patches and coral-covered reefs, from 4-30 m.

Characters   Black chevron markings on a pale ground color, separated by a broad white band from a red patch on rear and upper portion of body and adjacent fins; orange bar through eye (silvery edge above) and silver-edged black marking on nape; caudal fin with submarginal red bar. Juveniles same as adult, but with black spot on soft dorsal fin. Reaches 14 cm. Similar in appearance to *Chaetodon mertensii* (page 120), which differs in having orange (rather than red) pigmentation at the rear of the body.

Remarks   Commonly seen in pairs or small aggregations. An omnivorous species that feeds on coral polyps, algae, polychaetes and crustaceans. A member of the *xanthurus* species complex, which also contains *C. xanthurus* (page 119) from the western Pacific and the widely distributed *C. mertensii* (page 120).

Distribution   Restricted to the Red Sea and neighboring Gulf of Aden.

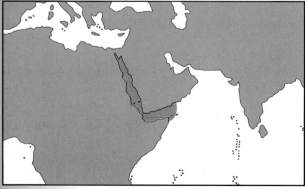

Chaetodon litus
Easter Island Butterflyfish
Randall & Caldwell 1973

John E. Randall

Habitat Rocky reefs composed of volcanic boulders, with prolific growth of brown algae, from 1-25 m. Juveniles in shallow tide pools with some coral growth.

Characters Dusky brownish-gray with slightly darker head; soft portions of fins slightly darker than body; rear edge of caudal fin, and margin of anal fin white; front edge of pelvic fin white. Juveniles similar to adult, slightly paler and more silvery overall. Attains 15 cm.

Remarks A subtropical species which inhabits waters ranging in temperature from about 20-22°C. Along with *Forcipiger flavissimus* (page 183) this butterflyfish is one of only two members of the family occurring at remote Easter Island. Juveniles have been observed picking ectoparasites from other fishes.

Distribution Restricted to Easter Island in the southeastern Pacific Ocean.

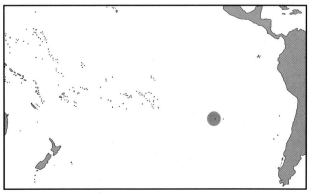

Chaetodon rafflesi
Latticed Butterflyfish
Bennett 1830

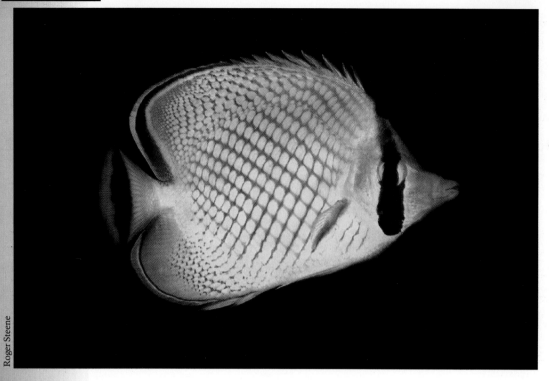

Roger Steene

Habitat Sheltered coastal reefs, lagoons, and outer slopes, usually in rich coral areas, to about 15 m depth.

Characters Yellow with dark scale margins giving a lattice-like appearance; black eye-bar and blue pigmentation between eyes; broad dark submarginal band on soft dorsal fin; central black bar on caudal fin. Juvenile similar to adult but with a dark spot on soft dorsal fin. Grows to maximum size of 15 cm.

Remarks Most common on sheltered coastal reefs where visibility is often reduced. Usually occurs singly or in pairs. Juveniles shelter among branching corals. Feeds on a variety of items including coral polyps, anemones, and polychaetes.

Distribution Indo-west Pacific region, from Sri Lanka to the Tuamotu Islands. Northwards to southern Japan, and south to the Great Barrier Reef.

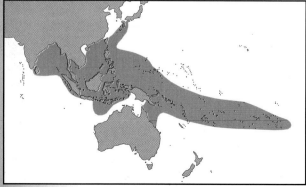

Chaetodon semeion
Dotted Butterflyfish
Bleeker 1855

Gerald R. Allen

Habitat Areas of prolific coral growth in clear water on lagoonal and semi-protected outer reef slopes. Ranges in depth from 2-50 m, but is most common above 25 m.

Characters Golden-yellow overall with many horizontal rows of small black dots on sides; black eye-bar and prominent blue marking from forehead to snout; broad submarginal black bands on soft dorsal and anal fins; dorsal fin ends in a filament. Grows to a maximum of 24 cm.

Remarks Relatively uncommon throughout its range, and more cautious than most butterflyfish species. Pairs are most often encountered, but small shoals sometimes observed. Black eye bar gradually reduces in size with increasing age. Some specimens with a large dusky patch above pectoral fin tip.

Distribution Throughout the Indo-west and central Pacific from Sri Lanka to the Tuamotu Islands. Northwards to the Ryukyu Islands and south as far as the Great Barrier Reef.

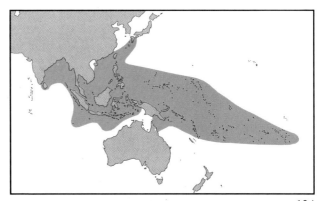

Chaetodon blackburni
Blackburn's Butterflyfish
Desjardins 1836

Roger Steene

Habitat Rocky reefs with scattered coral growth, from 10-55 m.

Characters Ground color variable, from light to dark brown with series of diagonal lines on side; black bar through eye; snout, breast and rear part of head pale; caudal fin base white becoming transparent at edge. Reaches 13 cm in length. Darker individuals bear a superficial resemblance to *Chaetodon dialeucos* (opposite) , but that species has a black caudal fin.

Remarks Found alone or in pairs. An omnivorous species which feeds on small crevice dwelling invertebrates, including amphipods and polychaetes, as well as zooplankton.

Distribution Western Indian Ocean on the East African coast from Kenya to Bashee (South Africa). Also found at Madagascar and the Mascarene Islands.

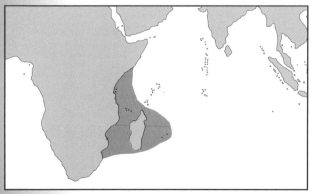

Chaetodon dialeucos
Oman Butterflyfish
Salm & Mee 1989

Helmut Debelius/Ikan

Habitat Rock and rubble slopes, also around coral patches on sandy slopes from 5-25 m.

Characters Dark overall with black scale edges forming a network pattern over the body; broad silvery bar behind head; head and eye black, with a silvery snout. Attains 15 cm. Similar to *Chaetodon blackburni* (opposite), but differs in having a black (rather than pale) caudal fin.

Remarks Usually found in pairs, but also encountered singly or in larger aggregations. Diet is mostly composed of benthic invertebrates and algae.

Distribution Known only from the Arabian Sea along the coast of Oman.

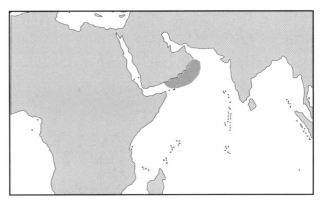

Chaetodon nigropunctatus
Black-Spotted Butterflyfish
Sauvage 1880

Gerald R. Allen

Habitat Shallow coral or rocky reefs and sandy lagoons, between 2-18 m.

Characters Variable ground color from dark brown to yellowish brown over body and all fins; scale centers black giving spotted appearance; snout and lower portion of head white; median fins with black margin; caudal fin mostly brown with a transparent edge, and with white and black submarginal bands. Population from the Gulf of Oman is typically more yellowish, especially on soft portions of fins. Attains 13 cm.

Remarks A home-ranging species which occurs either singly or paired. Coral polyps form the bulk of the diet.

Distribution Northwestern Indian Ocean including Arabian Gulf southwards to central Oman.

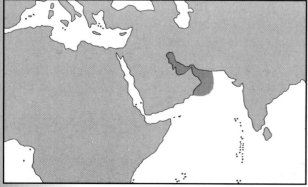

Chaetodon flavirostris
Black Butterflyfish
Günther 1873

Roger Steene

Sub-adult

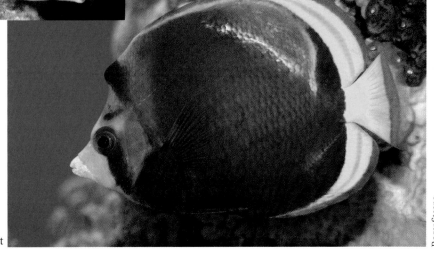

Adult

Roger Steene

Habitat Outer and more sheltered inner reefs in areas of rich coral growth. Also occasionally found in estuaries, as well as rocky areas dominated by algal growth. Depth from 2-20 m. Juveniles prefer protected inner reefs.

Characters Mostly dark with yellow patch (varying in brightness) adjacent to soft dorsal fin; head grayish and with a yellow snout and white mouth; dorsal, caudal, and anal fins yellow with a central orange band on soft portions and a dark margin. Juvenile similar to adult but with paler head. Reaches 20 cm.

Remarks Most commonly seen alone or in pairs, but forms larger aggregations at some localities (e.g. Lord Howe Island). Feeds on coral polyps, algae, and benthic invertebrates. A timid species on the Great Barrier Reef, but more approachable elsewhere.

Distribution Southwestern Pacific region from the Great Barrier Reef to coastal New South Wales and Lord Howe Island. Range extends eastward to New Caledonia, Fiji, Samoa, Rapa, and Pitcairn Island.

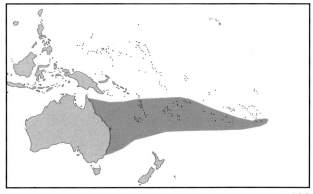

Chaetodon burgessi
Burgess' Butterflyfish
Allen & Starck 1973

Dieter Eichler

Habitat Vertical or undercut drop-offs on outer reefs, around gorgonians and black coral in deeper water, between 20-80 m. Usually below 40 m.

Characters White head and body with three separate black markings; one through eye, a second behind head to pectoral fin , a third encompassing the entire upper rear portion of the body and fins from the origin of dorsal fin to the corner of the anal fin; caudal fin white at base, becoming transparent. Maximum size about 14 cm.

Remarks An infrequently sighted fish, usually occurring in pairs. Similar in shape and coloration to several closely related species including *C. mitratus* (opposite), *C. tinkeri* (page 132), *C. flavocoronatus* (page 131), and *C. declivis* (page 133). *C. burgessi* is easily distinguished on the basis of its unique color pattern. Presumed hybrids between this species and *C. flavocoronatus/C. tinkeri* have been recorded from the Gilbert Islands.

Distribution Probably widespread in the western Pacific region, but has not been widely collected or observed due to its relatively deep habitat. Confirmed distribution records include Indonesia (Flores and Sulawesi), Sabah (Sipadan I.), Palau, Philippines, Papua New Guinea (New Britain) and Pohnpei.

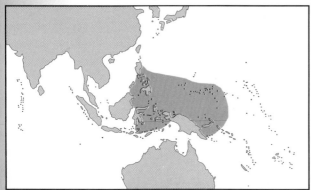

Chaetodon mitratus
Indian Butterflyfish
Günther 1860

Roger Steene

Habitat   Steep outer reef slopes and drop-offs with growth of black corals and sea fans. Also deep rubble areas. Ranges in depth from 22-80 m, but usually encountered below 50 m.

Characters   Pelvic fins and body pale yellowish, becoming pale bluish on upper body; two broad black diagonal bands with light blue margins tapering towards anal fin; bar through eye, black above and orange below; posterior section of dorsal fin orange-yellow. The Mauritius population is more yellow overall compared to other localities. Maximum size about 14 cm. Most similar in appearance and closely related to *Chaetodon burgessi* (opposite), which is paler overall and has an entirely black dorsal fin.

Remarks   Occurs alone, in pairs or small groups. Feeds on benthic invertebrates and planktonic items. Belongs to the subgenus *Roa*, which also contains *Chaetodon tinkeri* (page 132), *C. flavocoronatus* (page 131), *C. declivis* (page 133) and *C. burgessi*.

Distribution   Scattered localities throughout the Indian Ocean including Cocos-Keeling Atoll, Christmas Island, the Maldives, Mauritius, Amirante, Cosmoledo, and Chagos Islands.

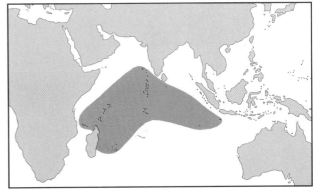

Chaetodon flavocoronatus
Yellow-Crowned Butterflyfish
Myers 1980

★ ★ ★

Robert Myers

Habitat   Steep drop-offs and vertical walls where currents are strong and growth of gorgonians and black coral is abundant, from 35-75 m.

Characters   White ground color with numerous black dots and a diagonally demarcated black patch on rear upper corner of body and adjacent fins; dorsal fin with yellow margin; three yellow markings on head (on top of snout, an eye-band, and a band from nape to level of eye); base of caudal fin yellow. Maximum size 12 cm. Similar to *Chaetodon tinkeri* (opposite), which differs in lacking the orange band on the nape as described above.

Remarks   Rarely sighted, this species is known on the basis of only a few specimens. Found alone or in pairs. Closely related, and similar in shape and coloration to several species including *C. tinkeri*, *C. mitratus* (page 130), *C. burgessi* (page 129), and *C. declivis* (page 133).

Distribution   Known only from Guam (Orote Peninsula) in the Mariana Islands.

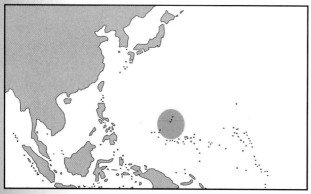

Chaetodon tinkeri
Tinker's Butterflyfish
Schultz 1951

Gerald R. Allen

Habitat Steep outer reef slopes and drop-offs among black corals and gorgonians, in relatively deep water from 27-160 m, usually below 40 m.

Characters Mostly white with numerous small black spots on body and large triangular black patch covering entire rear upper portion of body and fins; orange submarginal markings on dorsal fin; black edged yellow-orange bar through eye and yellow marking on tip of snout; caudal fin also yellow-orange. Reaches maximum of about 15 cm. Similar in appearance to *Chaetodon flavocoronatus* (opposite), which has an additional yellow band on the head.

Remarks Solitary individuals, pairs, and small aggregations are encountered. Diverse diet consists of both planktonic and benthic items. Hybrids between this species and *Chaetodon miliaris* (page 100) have been recorded in the wild. Specimens from the Marshall Islands have more extensive yellow near the edge of the dorsal fin.

Distribution Known only from a few locations in the central Pacific Ocean including the Hawaiian Islands, Johnston Atoll, and the Marshall Islands (Enewetak Atoll). Possibly more widespread, but remains undetected because of its preference for deep water.

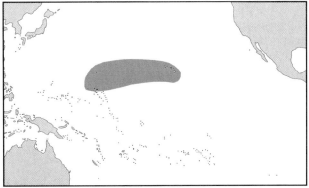

Chaetodon declivis
Marquesan Butterflyfish
Randall 1975

John E. Randall

Habitat Rocky reef slopes and steep walls adjacent to sandy bottoms, usually below 20 m.

Characters White overall with numerous dark spots on body; diagonally demarcated orange patch on upper rear portion of body and fins, from dorsal fin origin to just below caudal-fin base; dark spot on caudal-fin base; orange bar through eye; caudal, pelvic and anal fins yellowish. Maximum size about 12 cm. Similar to *Chaetodon tinkeri* (page 132), which differs in having a black rather than orange diagonally demarcated patch.

Remarks Two subspecies are currently recognized: *C. declivis declivis*, from the Marquesas Islands, and; *C. declivis wilderi*, from the Line Islands (brighter yellow bar through eye and more black coloration on the prominent orange patch). Specific name (*declivis*) translates to 'sloping' and refers to the diagonal demarcation of the color pattern.

Distribution Known only from the Marquesas and Line Islands in the South Pacific Ocean.

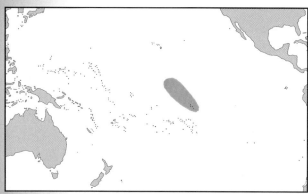

Chaetodon smithi
Smith's Butterflyfish
Randall 1975

John E. Randall

Habitat   Rocky algal-covered reefs, with scattered coral growth, from 10-30 m.

Characters   Very distinctive two-tone color pattern, dark brown (almost black) on head, front part of body and adjacent fins, and yellow on posterior half; iridescent blue margins on soft portions of dorsal and anal fins; caudal fin mostly yellow with a transparent edge. Maximum size approximately 17 cm.

Remarks   Not discovered until 1967, undoubtedly due to its restricted and remote distribution. Commonly occurs in large mid-water feeding aggregations. Diet consists mainly of zooplankton. When threatened, individuals rapidly seek refuge in the reef. Very similar habits to *Hemitaurichthys* species (see pages 185-188).

Distribution   Restricted to the remote southeastern corner of Polynesia. Known only from Rapa, Pitcairn and Illots de Bass (Marotiri).

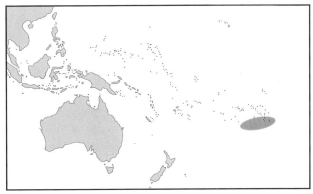

Chaetodon collare
Collare Butterflyfish
Bloch 1787

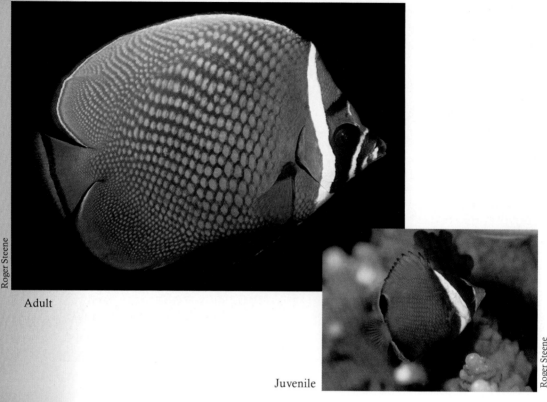

Roger Steene

Adult

Juvenile

Roger Steene

Habitat Rocky shoreline reefs and coral-rich outer reefs, in relatively shallow water from 1-20 m.

Characters Adult: Dark overall with pale scale centers; white bar behind eye and narrow white line behind mouth; caudal fin mostly red with white and black marginal and submarginal bands. Juvenile: Body more predominantly red-orange than adult; head mostly white with dark bar through eye. Attains 16 cm. Juvenile superficially resembles *Chaetodon auripes* (page 105), however it may be distinguished by the red tail base.

Remarks Usually seen in pairs but forms large aggregations of about 25 or more individuals. Feeds primarily on coral polyps and polychaetes, but consumes algae in areas where coral growth is scarce. Relatively easy to approach.

Distribution Northern Indian Ocean from the southern portion of the Arabian Peninsula and Gulf of Oman, east to Indonesia and the Philippines. Also common at the Maldives.

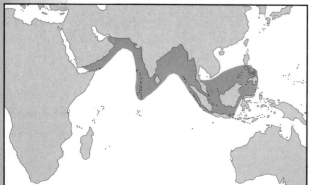

Chaetodon reticulatus
Reticulated Butterflyfish
Cuvier 1831

Roger Steene

Habitat   Most common on exposed outer reefs from 1-30 m, but occasionally found in coral-rich lagoons.

Characters   Black with pale scale centers (giving spotted appearance), becoming white dorsally; broad white-edged black bar through eye and black mouth; broad white area behind head; black-edged yellow submarginal band on tail and anal fins; central bluish-white bar on caudal fin; reddish marking on upper edge of anal fin. Reaches a maximum size of 16 cm. Resembles *Chaetodon collare* (opposite), which lacks white color on upper back and adjacent dorsal fin, and has red caudal fin.

Remarks   Usually in pairs, but solitary individuals and small aggregations are also encountered. Diet is comprised mainly of coral polyps. A relatively fearless species, easily approached underwater. Juveniles lack the red marking on the anal fin.

Distribution   Western and central Pacific Ocean, from the Philippines to Polynesia (including Hawaiian Is., Marquesas, Ducie I.). Northern extreme of range is the Ryukyu and Bonin Islands, southern limit is New Caledonia and the Austral Islands.

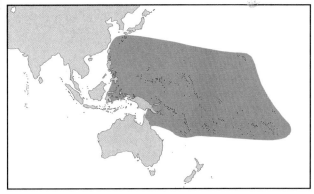

136

Chaetodon meyeri
Meyer's Butterflyfish
Bloch & Schneider 1801

Roger Steene

Habitat   Areas of rich coral in clear water lagoons and on seaward reefs, from 2-25 m.

Characters   White to bluish-white with series of diagonal and curving black bands converging towards pectoral region; black bars on snout, through eye and on gill cover separated by gold bars; all fins yellow including pectorals; median fins with black submarginal bands. Maximum size about 18 cm. *Chaetodon ornatissimus* (opposite) is similar in appearance but has orange bands on the side.

Remarks   Adults occur either paired or solitary and exhibit home-ranging behavior. Juveniles are usually observed among branching corals. Feeds exclusively on coral polyps. Never common anywhere throughout its range.

Distribution   Indo-west and central Pacific, from East Africa to the Line Islands, north as far as the Ryukyu Islands and south to the Great Barrier Reef.

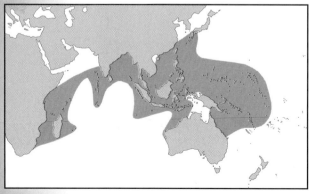

Chaetodon ornatissimus
Ornate Butterflyfish
Cuvier 1831

Roger Steene

Habitat Clear waters of rich coral areas in lagoons and on outer reefs (especially in areas exposed to mild surge, e.g. reef crests) usually in the vicinity of drop-offs. Depth range is from 1-36 m.

Characters Bluish-white with about six oblique (nearly horizontal) orange bands on side; head with alternating black and gold bars including a black bar through eye, also triangular grayish patch between eyes; caudal fin bluish-white with black submarginal band and central black bar. Maximum size about 18 cm. Similar in appearance to *Chaetodon meyeri* (opposite), which has black oblique markings on the side.

Remarks A shy, relatively uncommon species which is almost always encountered in pairs. Feeds exclusively on coral polyps and exhibits home-ranging behavior. Juveniles occur singly among the branches of hard corals.

Distribution Widespread in the Indo-west Pacific region from Sri Lanka to Polynesia (including Hawaiian Is., Marquesas, Ducie I.), north to southern Japan and south to Lord Howe and Rapa Island.

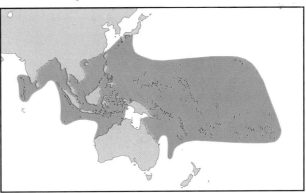

138

Chaetodon ephippium
Saddled Butterflyfish
Cuvier 1831

Adult

Juvenile

Habitat   Areas of rich coral growth in lagoons and on outer reefs from 1-30 m.

Characters   Easily recognized by the large black patch with a white border on the rear upper corner of the body and dorsal fin (which forms an elongate filament in large adults); body light gray with several blue-gray stripes below the middle of side; breast and snout yellow; very narrow and short eye band. Grows to a maximum size of 23 cm. Juveniles similar to adult, but with more prominent eye band and without filamentous dorsal fin or blue stripes on side.

Remarks   One of the most distinctive butterflyfishes. Occurs solitary, paired or in small groups. The diet includes coral polyps, algae, sponges, fish eggs and benthic invertebrates. Hybrids of this species and the closely-related *Chaetodon xanthocephalus* (opposite) have been reported at the Similan Islands and Sri Lanka.

Distribution   Widely distributed throughout the central and western Pacific to southern Japan, the Hawaiian, Marquesas and Tuamotu islands. Southern limit of distribution is New South Wales and Rapa Island Also ranging to the Indian Ocean at least as far west as Sri Lanka.

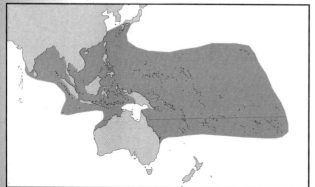

Chaetodon xanthocephalus
Yellow-Head Butterflyfish
Bennett 1832

Adult

Roger Steene

Juvenile

Roger Steene

Habitat   Rocky reefs rich in algae, and coral-rich areas of lagoons, to depths of 25 m.

Characters   Adult: Pale grayish overall with several narrow bluish-gray chevron markings on sides; head and breast yellow-orange; soft portions of dorsal and anal fins yellow-orange to olive with pale yellow margins; broad white band bellow dorsal fin; caudal fin transparent. Juvenile: Whitish with rim of yellow-orange around entire body and fins (except caudal); dark bar through eye; dark patch on soft dorsal fin and dark spot on tail base. Attains 20 cm.

Remarks   Roams widely over reefs in search of live coral food. Generally found alone, but sometimes seen in pairs. Most closely related to *Chaetodon ephippium* (opposite) and hybrids between these two species have been observed at Sri Lanka and the Similan Islands (Andaman Sea).

Distribution   Relatively widespread in the Indian Ocean. Occurs along the East African coast from Durban to Somalia, also at Madagascar, Chagos Archipelago, Mascarenes, Maldives and Sri Lanka.

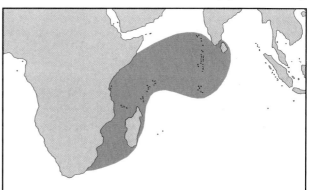

140

Chaetodon fasciatus
Red Sea Raccoon Butterflyfish
Forsskål 1775

Roger Steene

Habitat Coral-rich areas, especially reef flats, from 2 to at least 25 m depth.

Characters Yellow-orange overall with series of diagonal black bands on side (some individuals with entire upper part of body darkened); black patch surrounding eye connected across forehead, white band immediately above this patch (giving raccoon appearance); black patch at front of body, just below anterior part of dorsal fin. Juveniles with an ocellus on soft dorsal fin. Attains 25 cm. Resembles the closely-related *Chaetodon lunula* (opposite), which differs in several color-pattern features including a back marking across the tail base.

Remarks Occurs solitary or in pairs. Feeds on coral polyps, algae and benthic invertebrates. Relatively easy to approach underwater.

Distribution Restricted to the Red Sea and adjacent Gulf of Aden.

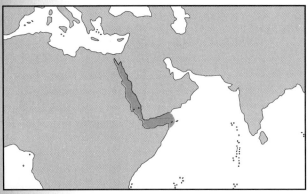

Chaetodon lunula
Raccoon Butterflyfish
(Lacépède 1803)

Roger Steene

Habitat   Lagoons and outer reefs to at least 30 m. Most commonly observed in rocky areas, either slopes or in the intertidal zone (especially juveniles).

Characters   Adult: Yellow-orange overall, more dusky on upper half of body, with series of diagonal lines on side; black patch around eye, with white band behind eye across forehead; two broad yellow-edged black bands behind head, and black spot on caudal-fin base (distinguishes this species from *Chaetodon fasciatus* - opposite). Juvenile similar, but with an ocellus on soft dorsal fin and a black patch posterior to white head band. Maximum size approximately 21 cm.

Remarks   Occurs singly, paired, or in small aggregations. The only nocturnally active butterflyfish species, foraging mostly at night and occasionally during the day. Favored food items include nudibranchs, tubeworm tentacles, coral polyps and algae.

Distribution   Widespread throughout the Indo-west and central Pacific, from East Africa to Polynesia (including Hawaiian Is., Marquesas, Ducie I.). Extends northwards to southern Japan and south to Lord Howe and Rapa Island. Vagrants occasionally seen in the eastern Pacific at the Galapagos.

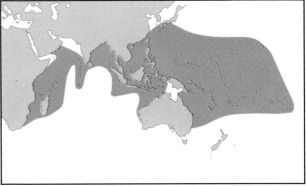

Chaetodon pelewensis
Dot and Dash Butterflyfish
Kner 1868

Roger Steene

Habitat   Outer reefs with substantial cover of live coral, to at least 30 m depth.

Characters   Yellowish tan with diagonal rows of dark spots, becoming solid bands on rear upper parts of body (sometimes erratic arrangement); dark-edged orange bar through eye and black spot on nape; median fins with submarginal black line; base of caudal fin orange. Attains 12.5 cm. Almost identical in color to *Chaetodon punctatofasciatus* (opposite), which differs in having vertical (rather than oblique) bars on the side.

Remarks   Usually occurs in pairs, sometimes with *C. punctatofasciatus*. Individuals with unusual color patterns recorded from the northern Great Barrier Reef and New Guinea may represent hybrids of these two species. Feeds mostly on coral polyps, but also consumes benthic invertebrates.

Distribution   Southern Pacific Ocean, from Papua New Guinea to the Tuamotus. South to Lord Howe Island. Abundant on the Great Barrier Reef and in the Coral Sea.

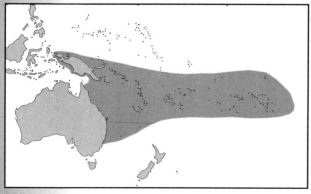

Chaetodon punctatofasciatus
Spot-Banded Butterflyfish
Cuvier 1831

Habitat   Most common on outer reef slopes, but also occurs in clear water lagoons and reef flats with rich coral growth, from 1-45 m.

Characters   Yellowish tan becoming yellowish dorsally with about seven vertical dark bars on upper body and rows of dark spots below; dark-edged orange bar through eye and black spot on nape; median fins with submarginal black line; tail base orange. Attains 12 cm. Almost identical to *Chaetodon pelewensis* (opposite), but that species has dark spots arranged in oblique diagonal rows.

Remarks   A relatively shy fish, usually occurring in pairs (sometimes with *C. pelewensis*). Diet is comprised primarily of coral polyps, but algae and benthic invertebrates also consumed. Closely related to *C. pelewensis* and probably hybridizes with this species at some localities (e.g. New Guinea, Great Barrier Reef).

Distribution   Mainly distributed throughout the western Pacific, from western Indonesia to the Line Islands, but straying to Christmas Island in the Indian Ocean. Also ranging north to the Ryukyu Islands and south to the Great Barrier Reef.

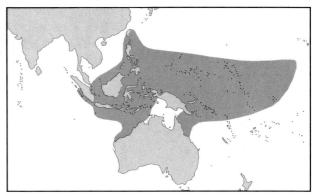

Chaetodon guttatissimus
Spotted Butterflyfish
Bennett 1832

Roger Steene

Habitat Coral reef areas of lagoons and seaward slopes to a depth of 25 m.

Characters Pale beige ground color with distinctive speckling on sides; black bar through eye to forehead (some orange below eye); soft portions of dorsal and anal fins grayish (due to closely spaced dark spots) with a yellowish beige margin and black submarginal band; caudal fin beige at base, transparent to edge, with a central dark bar. Maximum size about 12 cm. Belongs to a complex of species including *C. punctatofasciatus* (page 144), *C. pelewensis* (page 143), and *C. multicinctus* (opposite). Although closely related, they are easily separated on the basis of color pattern.

Remarks Occurs singly, in pairs, or in small groups. Feeds on coral polyps, polychaetes, and algae.

Distribution Wide ranging throughout the Indian Ocean from the coast of East Africa (northwards of Durban) to Christmas Island, and the Andaman Sea coast of western Thailand.

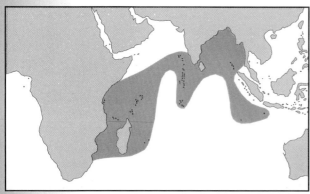

Chaetodon multicinctus
Multiband Butterflyfish
Garrett 1863

John E. Randall

Habitat Lagoon and seaward reef areas with prolific coral growth (particularly *Porites* and *Pocillopora*) between 5-30 m.

Characters Whitish with series of about 4-6 gold-brown bars on side and many faint spots covering the body and adjacent fins; bar through eye ending before forehead and black spot on nape; black bar on caudal-fin base and central black bar on caudal fin. Grows to maximum length of 12 cm.

Remarks Frequently observed in pairs or small aggregations. An omnivorous species, the diet consisting of coral polyps, polychaetes, small crustaceans and algae. Juveniles present on shallow inshore reefs from April to September.

Distribution Restricted to the Hawaiian Islands and Johnston Atoll.

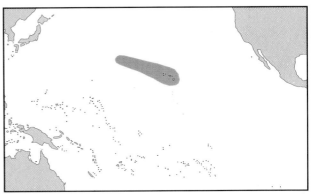

Chaetodon citrinellus
Speckled Butterflyfish
Cuvier 1831

★ ★

Roger Steene

Habitat Moderately exposed (to surf) inner reef flats, lagoons, and outer reefs, usually in 1-3 m, but occasionally as deep as 36 m. Often seen in very shallow areas where coral growth is sparse.

Characters Ground color varies, from white to bright yellow, speckled with many faint dots on side; black bar through eye; bottom edge of anal fin black; caudal fin transparent. Reaches a maximum of 13 cm. Bears a superficial resemblance to several other species including *C. miliaris* (page 100), *C. assarius* (page 99), *C. dolosus* (page 101), and *C. guentheri* (page 102), but is unique in having a black anal fin margin.

Remarks Relatively common throughout its distribution. An aggressive species which commonly adopts a defensive posture, facing downwards with dorsal spines erect, when threatened. Feeds on coral polyps, algae and polychaete worms. Often occurs in pairs but also forms small shoals.

Distribution Widely distributed throughout the Indo-west and central Pacific from East Africa to the Hawaiian, Marquesas and Tuamotu islands. North as far as southern Japan and south to Lord Howe Island.

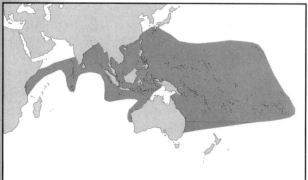

Chaetodon fremblii
Blue-Striped Butterflyfish
Bennett 1828

Habitat Prefers rocky areas, but also occurs on coral reefs, from 4 to at least 65 m. Juveniles frequent shallow, protected reef flats from April to September.

Characters Generally yellow-orange, but sometimes paler overall; series of narrow light blue diagonal bands on side, adjacent fins, and head; black spot on nape and larger black patch at rear of body, anterior to caudal fin; caudal fin white at base and yellow submarginally. Attains 13 cm.

Remarks Solitary or in small groups of about 3-15 individuals. Omnivorous, feeding on coral polyps, benthic invertebrates and fish eggs.

Distribution Restricted to the Hawaiian Islands, most common around the southeastern part.

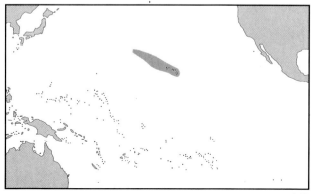

Chaetodon excelsa
Hawaiian Brown-Banded Butterflyfish
(Jordan 1922)

John E. Randall

Habitat	Rocky areas, sometimes as shallow as 20 m but usually much deeper, to 200 m.
Characters	Body white with two broad brown bars with darkened borders extending onto adjacent fins, a third brown bar from forehead through eye; dark snout stripe; oval shaped ocellus on soft dorsal fin; pelvic fin mostly black with narrow white anterior edge; caudal fin transparent. Maximum size about 17 cm.
Remarks	Belongs to a complex of closely related, similar looking species including *C. jayakari* (opposite) and C. *modestus* (page 151). All three species are nearly identical in appearance, varying only slightly in the shape of the ocellus and in depth of the caudal fin base. They have widely separated distributions and are therefore not likely to be confused in the field. Feeds mostly on benthic invertebrates.
Distribution	Only recorded from the Hawaiian Islands and Guam, but probably more widespread in deep waters of the central Pacific.

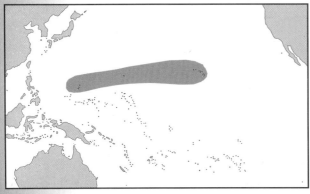

149

Chaetodon jayakari
Jayakar's Butterflyfish
Norman 1939

John E. Randall

Habitat Frequents relatively deep water, 33-274 m.

Characters Silvery-white with two broad brownish bars on side; a third, narrower brown bar through eye; rounded white-edged ocellus on soft dorsal fin, enclosed by second body bar; narrow white bar posterior to second brown body bar; caudal fin transparent. Maximum size about 17 cm.

Remarks A member of the *modestus* species complex. Almost identical in shape, coloration and fin-ray counts to *Chaetodon excelsa* (opposite) and *C. modestus* (page 151), however *C. jayakari* has an ocellus which is reportedly more rounded. Other, less obvious, proportional differences exist within this complex (e.g. depth of caudal-fin base, length of various fin spines). Confusion of these three species in the field is precluded by their widely separated geographic distributions.

Distribution Northwestern Indian Ocean from the west coast of India to the Red Sea.

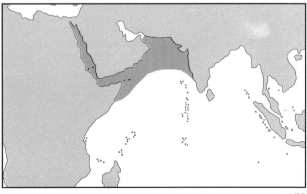

150

Chaetodon modestus
Brown-Banded Butterflyfish
Temminck & Schlegel 1842

Kiyoshi Endoh

Habitat Rocky reefs in deep water. At tropical localities it ranges between 110-250 m, but occurs as shallow as 40 m in temperate waters of Japan.

Characters Silvery-white with two broad brownish bars on side extending to adjacent fins; a third, narrower brown bar through eye; ovate white-edged ocellus on soft dorsal fin, enclosed by second body bar; narrow white bar posterior to second brown body bar; caudal fin transparent, narrow brown bar on caudal fin base. Maximum size about 17 cm.

Remarks Forms aggregations. Belongs to a group of closely related species including *Chaetodon excelsa* (page 149) from Hawaii and Guam and *C. jayakari* (page 150) from the northern Indian Ocean. The three are virtually identical in color, being distinguishable only on the basis of a few proportional measurements and fin ray counts. Unlikely to be confused in the wild given their widely separated distributions.

Distribution Western Pacific region, from southern Japan to Western Australia.

Chaetodon marleyi
South African Butterflyfish
Regan 1921

Gerald R. Allen

Habitat	Rocky and coral covered reefs to 120 m depth. Also occurs in shallow tide pools and estuarine environments among weed beds.
Characters	Silvery-white overall with yellow scale centers and series of brownish bars, including one through eye, two broader bars on body, one on caudal-fin base, and one centrally on caudal fin; black spot at top of second body bar; anal and pelvic fins yellow. Juveniles with a second spot on the soft dorsal fin. Closely related to *Chaetodon hoefleri* (page 215). The adults of these two species are nearly identical, but the juvenile of *C. hoefleri* lack the additional dorsal-fin spot.
Remarks	A subtropical species which frequents waters ranging in temperature between 18-20°C. It is the only butterflyfish occurring in both the Indian and Atlantic Oceans.
Distribution	South African coastline from Lambert's Bay (Atlantic Ocean) to Delagoa Bay (Indian Ocean).

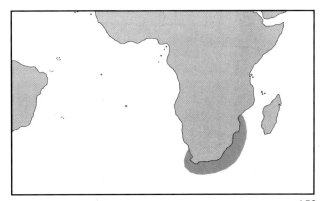

Chaetodon falcula
Saddle-Back Butterflyfish
Bloch 1793

Roger Steene

Habitat Areas of rich coral growth in lagoons and on seaward reefs from 1-15 m.

Characters Body mostly white becoming yellow dorsally, with series of narrow dark bars on side; pair of prominent wedge-shaped back bars on upper side; black bar through eye and on caudal-fin base; dorsal, anal and caudal fins yellow-orange. Maximum size about 20 cm. Color pattern similar to *Chaetodon ulietensis* (opposite), but that species lacks yellow on the back and the two prominent black markings are more faded and extend lower on the side.

Remarks Occurs in pairs or in large aggregations containing 20 or more individuals. An intrepid species that is easily approached.

Distribution Throughout the tropical Indian Ocean from East Africa to the Nicobar and Andaman Islands.

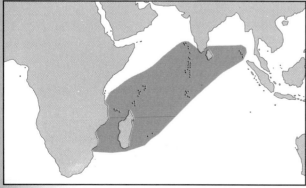

Chaetodon ulietensis
Pacific Double-Saddle Butterflyfish
Cuvier 1831

Roger Steene

Habitat Areas of prolific coral growth in lagoons and on outer reefs, particularly where currents are strong. Ranges to depths of 30 m.

Characters White with series of vertical black lines on sides and two broad dark bars on upper sides (anterior bar more faded); rear portion of body and adjacent fins yellow; black spot on tail base and black bar through eye. Attains 15 cm. Similar in appearance to *Chaetodon falcula* (opposite) from the Indian Ocean, however the dark bars of that species are more vivid and less extensive and surrounded by yellow.

Remarks Mostly seen in pairs, but also occurs singly or in aggregations. Large shoals sometimes occur at Tahiti and Fiji. Diverse diet includes a wide variety of invertebrates and algae.

Distribution Widespread throughout the central and western Pacific as far as the Tuamotu Islands. Range extends northwards to southern Japan and southwards to Lord Howe Island. Straying to Cocos-Keeling Atoll in the eastern Indian Ocean.

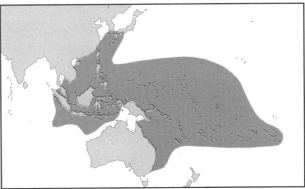

154

Chaetodon gardineri
Gardiner's Butterflyfish
Norman 1939

★ ★

Helmut Debelius/Ikan

Habitat Shallow continental shelf reefs from 2-40 m. Usually below 25 m at Sri Lanka.

Characters Head and body mostly white, speckled with numerous faint yellow dots, and extensive area of black pigmentation covering most of posterior body; black bar through eye, yellow on posterior edge; dorsal, anal, and base of caudal fin orange-yellow; margin of gill cover yellow. Maximum size about 17 cm. *Chaetodon leucopleura* (opposite) is similar, but has several narrow horizontal lines near the belly region, and dark pigmentation of lesser intensity covering a larger proportion of the body compared to *C. gardineri*.

Remarks Observed in pairs or small groups. Omnivorous diet includes algae and benthic invertebrates. The first author noted this species was sold at fish markets on a visit to Mutrah, near Muscat on the Gulf of Oman.

Distribution Northwestern Indian Ocean form the Arabian Peninsula to Sri Lanka.

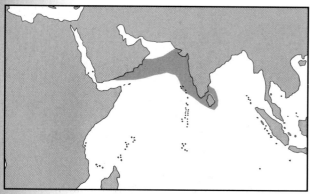

Chaetodon leucopleura
Somali Butterflyfish
Playfair 1866

Roger Steene

Habitat   Areas of rich live coral as well as open rubble bottoms, usually in deep water (40-80 m), but has been recorded as shallow as 7 m.

Characters   White with dark pigmentation over most of posterior and upper body, most intense near base of tail, faded elsewhere; black eye bar; all fins yellow except pectorals and rear edge of caudal fin; several dusky horizontal lines around belly region; margin of gill cover yellow, also yellow lines on snout. Maximum size about 18 cm. Closely related to *C. gardineri* (opposite) and *C. selene* (page 157). Similar in appearance to *C. gardineri*, which has more intense dark pigmentation on the body.

Remarks   Relatively uncommon, occurring either singly or in pairs. Scientific name refers to white (*leuco-*) sides (*-pleura*).

Distribution   Western Indian Ocean, East African coast from Zanzibar northwards to the southern Red Sea and Oman. Also at the Aldabra Islands and the Seychelles.

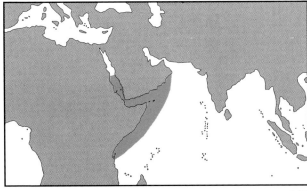

Chaetodon selene
Yellow-Dotted Butterflyfish
Bleeker 1853

Roger Steene

Habitat Coastal reefs, usually in moderately deep water (8-50 m) on rubble and sand slopes with scattered live coral outcrops.

Characters White with series of oblique rows of faint yellow dots on sides; dark bar through eye with yellow posterior margin, becomes entirely yellow below; black band with a yellow anterior edge below rear portions of median fins which are also yellow; caudal fin with transparent edge; yellow markings on snout and on margin of gill cover. Maximum size about 16 cm.

Remarks A rare species in most areas. Generally seen in pairs, although juveniles occur singly around coral outcrops. Adults prefer rubble or sandy bottoms where they forage on benthic invertebrates.

Distribution Western Pacific region, from Indonesia and western New Guinea, northwards through southeast Asia to southern Japan.

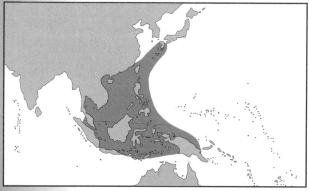

Chaetodon nippon
Japanese Butterflyfish
Steindachner & Döderlein 1884

Roger Steene

Habitat Rocky coastal reefs, from 5 to at least 20 m, but probably occurs much deeper.

Characters Adult: Mostly light yellowish-brown, becoming dark brown on posterior-most section of body and adjacent fins; head gray, lacking an eye-bar; yellow pelvic fins; caudal fin yellow with transparent edge. Juvenile: Similar coloration to adult, but ground color is more vibrant orange-yellow; there is an ocellus on the soft dorsal fin, and a dark eye bar is present. Maximum size about 15 cm.

Remarks Spawns in groups at sunset when water temperatures of at least 23°C prevail. In subtropical waters of Japan, temperatures as low as 16°C are common.

Distribution Western Pacific rim, from the northern Philippines to South Korea, also at southern Japan and the Izu Islands where it is common.

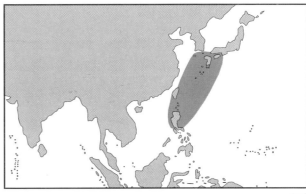

158

Chaetodon kleinii
Klein's Butterflyfish
Bloch 1790

Roger Steene

Habitat   Rocky reefs and coral-rich areas (sometimes interspersed with sandy bottoms) of lagoons, channels and outer reef slopes, from 2-61 m but usually below 10 m.

Characters   Body and adjacent fins mostly a dusky yellowish-brown, with a broad central pale bar; head white with black bar through eye to breast; small black spot on upper snout; pelvic fins black. Section of bar above eye becomes blue in adult specimens. Attains 14 cm.

Remarks   Occurs singly, in pairs, or occasionally in larger aggregations of up to about 30 individuals. In some areas it is the most abundant butterflyfish. Omnivorous diet consists mainly of soft corals, but also feeds on zooplankton and benthic invertebrates.

Distribution   Widespread throughout the Indo-west and central Pacific, from coastal East Africa to the Hawaiian Islands and Samoa, extending northwards to southern Japan and south to Lord Howe Island. Vagrants occasionally seen in the eastern Pacific at the Galapagos.

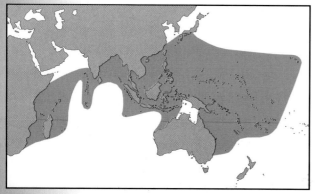

Chaetodon trichrous
Tahiti Butterflyfish
Günther 1874

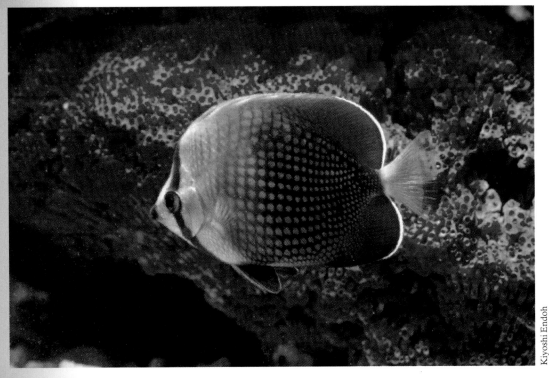

Kiyoshi Endoh

Habitat Mainly occurs on sheltered lagoon reefs, between 3-25 m.

Characters Head and front of body white, remainder of body and adjacent fins dark brown to black; black band through eye; caudal fin yellow with transparent edge. Attains 12 cm. Vaguely resembles the angelfish *Chaetodontoplus mesoleucus* (page 67), but the distributions of these species do not overlap. In any case, the cheek spine of *C. mesoleucus* readily distinguishes it from all butterflyfishes.

Remarks Usually not particularly abundant, but relatively common in lagoons at Tahiti. Solitary individuals, pairs and small aggregations of about 4-6 individuals have been observed. Closely related to *Chaetodon kleinii* (opposite), a more widespread ecological equivalent whose geographical distribution does not overlap.

Distribution Restricted to the Society Islands, Marquesas Islands, and Tuamotu Archipelago in the central-south Pacific Ocean.

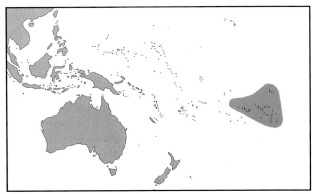

Chaetodon lineolatus
Lined Butterflyfish
Cuvier 1831

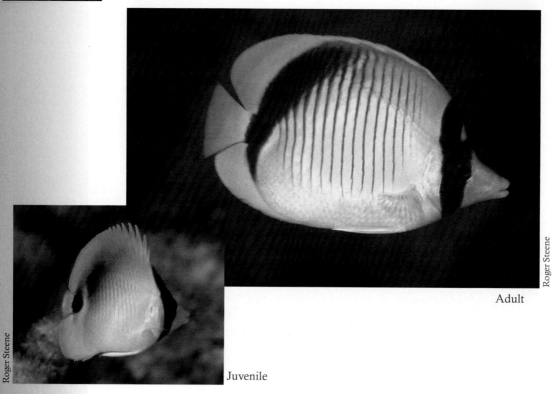

Adult

Roger Steene

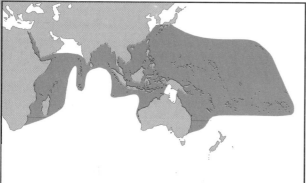

Juvenile

Roger Steene

Habitat Coral-rich areas of lagoons and seaward reefs, from 2-171 m.

Characters White overall with series of vertical black lines along side; broad black band, edged with yellow, along rear upper edge of body; wide black bar through eye to nape, enclosing a white spot on forehead; dorsal, caudal and anal fins yellow. Reaches a maximum size of 30 cm. Closely resembles *Chaetodon oxycephalus* (opposite), which differs in having an isolated black spot on the nape.

Remarks The largest of all butterflyfishes. Usually occurs in pairs, but solitary individuals and small aggregations are sometimes encountered. Diet is comprised mostly of coral polyps and anemones, but also includes benthic invertebrates and algae. A shy species that is often difficult to approach at close range.

Distribution Indo-west and central Pacific, from East Africa and the Red Sea to Polynesia (including Hawaiian Is., Ducie I.). North to southern Japan, and south to Lord Howe Island.

Chaetodon oxycephalus
Spot-Nape Butterflyfish
Bleeker 1853

Roger Steene

Habitat   Coral-rich areas, including both coastal and seaward reefs, in depths of 10-40 m.

Characters   White with many vertical black lines on side; black bar through eye and isolated black spot on nape (distinguishes this species from *Chaetodon lineolatus* [opposite] which has continuous bar between eye and nape); median fins yellow; broad black band below soft dorsal fin. Reaches maximum length of 25 cm.

Remarks   Usually found in pairs and feeds mostly on corals and anemones. Distribution of this species and closely related *C. lineolatus* overlaps, and they are sometimes seen on the same reefs in close proximity.

Distribution   Indo-west Pacific region, from the Maldives and Sri Lanka to Papua New Guinea. North to the Philippines and Palau, south to the Great Barrier Reef.

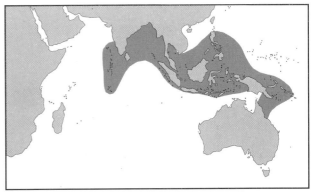

Chaetodon melannotus
Black-Backed Butterflyfish
Bloch & Schneider 1801

Roger Steene

Habitat　Coral-rich areas of lagoons, seaward reefs, and reef flats to 20 m depth.

Characters　White with series of diagonal black lines on sides; a broad black area below most of dorsal fin; all fins yellow except pectorals and rear edge of caudal fin which are white; yellow face with black bar through eye; small black spot near anal fin origin (absent in closely related *Chaetodon ocellicaudus*, opposite). Grows to a maximum of 15 cm.

Remarks　A home-ranging species, commonly observed browsing on live corals. Occurs singly or commonly in pairs. When observed there are usually several other conspecifics in the vicinity. Feeds mostly on polyps of soft and hard corals. Assumes different night time coloration: the entire dorsal section of the body turns black, enclosing two white blotches.

Distribution　Widespread throughout the Indo-west Pacific, from the Red Sea through the Indian Ocean to Samoa. Northern limit of range is southern Japan, southern limit is Lord Howe Island.

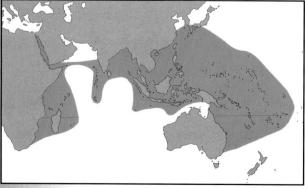

Chaetodon ocellicaudus
Spot-Tail Butterflyfish
Cuvier 1831

Roger Steene

Habitat Rich coral areas of lagoons and outer reefs, from 3-50 m. Most common on outer reef slopes and in reef crest channels.

Characters White with series of diagonal black lines on side; black bar through eye; anterior part of head, ventral section of body, and median fins yellow; numerous black dots at base of dorsal and anal fins; prominent black ocellus on caudal fin base (distinguishes this species from the similar *Chaetodon melannotus,* opposite). Juvenile similar to adult, but has darkened area along rear upper edge of body. Attains 14 cm.

Remarks Occurs singly or in pairs. Feeds mainly on polyps of both hard and soft corals.

Distribution Indo-Australian Archipelago from the Andaman Sea to Papua New Guinea. North to the Philippines and Palau, south to the northern Great Barrier Reef.

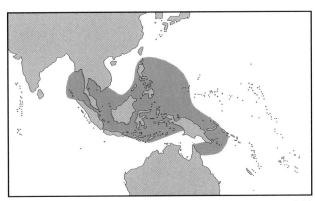

Chaetodon larvatus
Orange-Face Butterflyfish
Cuvier 1831

Gerald R. Allen

Habitat Clear waters of fringing reefs where plate-forming corals of the genus *Acropora* abound, from 3-12 m.

Characters Distinctly triangular-shaped body; pale gray with series of light chevron markings on side; head and breast a vivid red-orange with white posterior margin; soft dorsal fin and caudal fin black, edged with white. Reaches a maximum length of 12 cm.

Remarks A territorial species occurring singly or in pairs. Feeds exclusively on the polyps of plate-forming *Acropora* corals. Actively chases away other butterflyfishes encroaching on its food supply. Closely related to both *Chaetodon baronessa* (page 111) and *C. triangulum* (page 112) with which it shares similarities in body shape, coloration and behavior.

Distribution Known only from the Red Sea (Hurgada southwards) where it is common around Jeddah, and the adjacent Gulf of Aden.

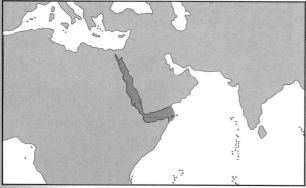

Chaetodon mesoleucos
White-Face Butterflyfish
Forsskål 1775

John E. Randall

Habitat Coral reefs and wrecks such as the "Umbria" near Port Sudan, to depths of at least 20 m.

Characters Body mostly grayish-brown with numerous close-set narrow black bars; head and front part of body silvery white with dark eye-bar (sometimes very faint); caudal fin white at base, with broad central black bar and transparent edge; pelvic fins white. Reaches maximum size of 16 cm.

Remarks An uncommon species which is sighted infrequently. Usually seen in pairs. Aggressive towards other butterflyfishes, at least under aquarium conditions.

Distribution Restricted to the Red Sea and Gulf of Aden.

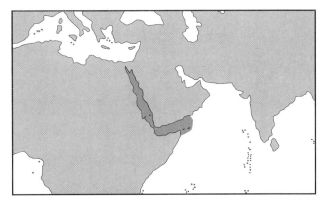

Chaetodon semilarvatus
Golden Butterflyfish
Cuvier 1831

Roger Steene

Habitat   Areas of rich coral growth in relatively shallow water (3-20 m).

Characters   Golden-yellow overall, with series of many closely spaced vertical (sometimes irregular) orange bars on sides; dark bluish-gray patch behind eye; light blue and black submarginal lines on rear part of dorsal and anal fins. Attains 23 cm.

Remarks   Very striking species in terms of appearance, usually fearless and easily approached underwater. Occurs in pairs and larger aggregations of up to about 20 individuals. Generally rests beneath *Acropora* plate corals during the day becoming active in late afternoon. Feeds primarily on the polyps of hard and soft corals.

Distribution   Restricted to the Red Sea and Gulf of Aden.

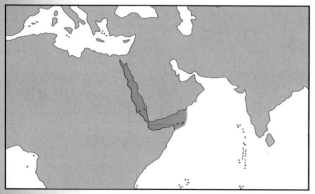

Chaetodon quadrimaculatus
Fourspot Butterflyfish
Gray 1831

John E. Randall

Habitat	Shallow, rocky reefs with some coral growth, from 2-15 m. Prefers areas exposed to surge activity.
Characters	Yellow-orange, with large dusky area on upper sides enclosing two white blotches; orange bar through eye with light blue margins; light blue submarginal bands on dorsal and anal fins; dark blotch in vicinity of tail base. Maximum size about 16 cm.
Remarks	Occurs solitary or in pairs. Diet consists primarily of *Pocillopora* coral polyps. An uncommon species at most localities except some areas of the Hawaiian Islands, such as the Kona coast. White blotches on sides disappear at night. Juveniles present in the Hawaiian Islands between May and September.
Distribution	Western and central Pacific Ocean, from Taiwan to Polynesia (including Hawaiian Is., Marquesas, Pitcairn I.), northwards to the Ryukyu and Bonin Islands.

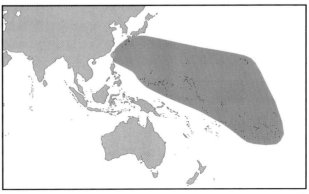

168

Chaetodon tricinctus
Three-Stripe Butterflyfish
Waite 1901

Roger Steene

Habitat Areas of rich coral growth in lagoons and on outer reefs, from 3-15 m.

Characters White becoming yellowish dorsally, with two broad black bars on body; a third narrower black bar through eye (becomes yellow ventrally); rear margin of dorsal and anal fins and base of caudal fin orange; pale bluish-green color on fins behind second body bar. Maximum size approximately 15 cm.

Remarks Generally occurs in pairs or small aggregations.

Distribution Known only from Lord Howe (abundant in the lagoon) and Norfolk Island in the southwestern corner of the Pacific Ocean. These isolated island outposts have an interesting fish community composed of a mixture of about 500 temperate and tropical species, including 16 endemics.

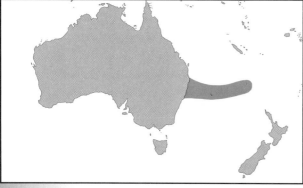

Chaetodon trifascialis
Chevroned Butterflyfish
Quoy & Gaimard 1824

Roger Steene

Habitat Areas where tabular and branching *Acropora* corals occur, including coastal, lagoonal, and outer reef habitats. Ranges to 30 m depth, but usually seen in 2-12 m.

Characters Adult: White with numerous black chevron markings on sides; black bar through eye; pelvic fins white; dorsal and anal fins yellowish to orange; caudal fin black with yellow-orange edges. Juvenile: Same as adult except with yellow pelvic fins, broad black band on rear of body, and yellow caudal fin (with black submarginal band). Reaches maximum size of 18 cm.

Remarks Territorial species which vigorously defends home corals, particularly against individuals belonging to the same species and the same sex and other coral-feeding butterflyfishes. Most commonly occurring singly, sometimes paired. Feeds primarily on the polyps and mucus of *Acropora* corals in the home territory, but small amounts of algae are also consumed. Each male's territory includes the territories of 2-3 females. Pair spawning occurs during the period of full and new moon. An unusually shaped butterflyfish formerly classified as a separate genus: *Megaprotodon*.

Distribution Very widespread throughout the Indo-west and central Pacific, from the Red Sea to the Hawaiian and Society Islands. North to southern Japan, and south to Lord Howe Island and Rapa.

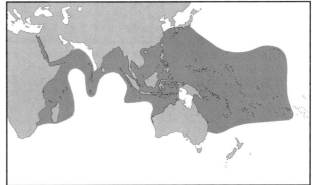

Chaetodon daedalma
Wrought Iron Butterflyfish
Jordan & Fowler 1903

Roger Steene

Habitat	Rocky shoreline reefs in clear, shallow water, to 7 m depth.
Characters	Black body and fins with variable amount of white speckling, and pale scale centers; mottled silver and black coloration on head; rear edge of dorsal, caudal and anal fins pale to yellow-orange. Maximum size about 15 cm.
Remarks	Forms large aggregations which range widely over rocky reefs grazing on algae and small benthic invertebrates. Specific name translates to adorned (*daedal-*).
Distribution	Occurs only around southern Japan and the nearby Ryukyu, Ogasawara, and Izu Islands. Relatively rare at most localities except at the Ogasawara Islands.

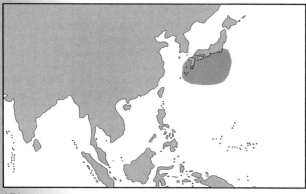

Chaetodon adiergastos
Panda Butterflyfish
Seale 1910

Roger Steene

Habitat Coral reefs in depths from 3-25 m, frequently observed near soft corals and on silty inshore reefs, but also common in clear water.

Characters Pale overall with faint diagonal striped markings on the body; large black patch surrounding eye, separate patch on forehead; dorsal, anal, and base of caudal fin yellow with black margin; pelvic fins also yellow. Juveniles have an ocellus on the soft dorsal fin. To 16 cm. Diagonal stripe pattern is similar to that seen in *Chaetodon ocellicaudus* (page 164) and *C. melannotus* (page 163), but both of these have a narrow dark bar through the eye, unlike *C. adiergastos*.

Remarks Usually occurs in pairs or small groups. Feeds on corals and various small invertebrates. A wary species which is sometimes difficult to approach.

Distribution Western Pacific rim and eastern Indian Ocean including the Ryukyu Islands, Taiwan, Philippines and Indonesia southwards to northwest Australia.

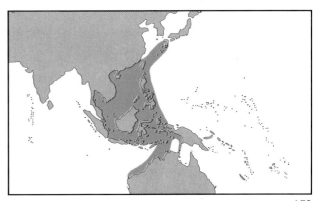

172

Chaetodon bennetti
Bennett's Butterflyfish
Cuvier 1831

Gerald R. Allen

Habitat   Lagoons and outer reefs where coral growth is prolific between 5-30 m.

Characters   Body yellow with large circular ocellus on upper side; two curving light blue lines originating at back of head and extending posteriorly to near beginning of anal fin; black bar with light blue edges through eye. Maximum size about 18 cm.

Remarks   Never common, usually seen solitary or in pairs. Feeds almost exclusively on coral polyps. Juveniles most often seen in shallower water among branching corals belonging to the genus *Acropora*. In some individuals, the ocellus appears as an indistinct dark blotch on the side.

Distribution   Widespread throughout the Indo-west and central Pacific from the coast of East Africa to the Pitcairn group. Northwards to southern Japan, south to Lord Howe Island and Rapa.

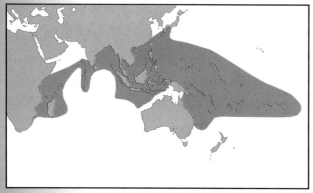

Chelmon muelleri
Müller's Coralfish
(Klunzinger 1879)

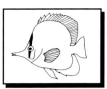

Roger Steene

Habitat Shallow coastal reefs with mud bottoms or extensive algal cover, as well as estuaries.

Characters Adult: Silvery-white ground color, becoming more golden posteriorly with three dark brown bars on sides; brown-edged orange bar through eye; narrow bar across tail base; soft portions of dorsal and anal fins brown; black spot on soft dorsal fin. Juvenile (illustrated): Similar to adult, except spot on soft dorsal fin forms ocellus and first two body bars more orange. Reaches maximum size of 18 cm.

Remarks Prefers silty or muddy areas lacking live coral cover, which are seldom explored by divers. Adults are usually encountered in pairs. Diet consists mostly of small benthic invertebrates. Large adults have a peculiar protuberance on nape.

Distribution Coastal tropical Australian waters, from northwest Western Australia to Queensland.

Chelmon marginalis
Margined Coralfish
Richardson 1842

Roger Steene

Habitat   Mainly coastal reefs and near shore islands from 1-30 m.

Characters   Adult: Silvery-white with two black-edged orange bars on head and front part of body; broad yellow-orange bar on rear of body; soft dorsal and anal fins yellow with orange and blue margin. Juvenile: Same as adult but with additional orange midbody bar and an ocellus on upper rear corner of body. Similar to closely related *Chelmon rostratus* (opposite), which has wider midbody bar. Reaches maximum size of 18 cm.

Remarks   Occurs either singly or in pairs. Juveniles assume adult coloration early, at size of 5-7 cm, but full transformation is very gradual. Sub-adults, with remnants of juvenile ocellus and faded midbody bar could be confused with *C. rostratus*, however, the spot is not an ocellus (without light outer rim) at this stage of development.

Distribution   Tropical Australian waters from northwest Western Australia to the northern Great Barrier Reef and coastal waters of Cape York Peninsula.

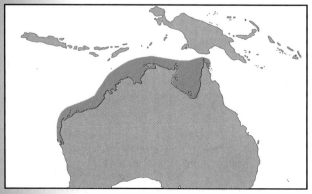

Chelmon rostratus
Beaked Coralfish
(Linnaeus 1758)

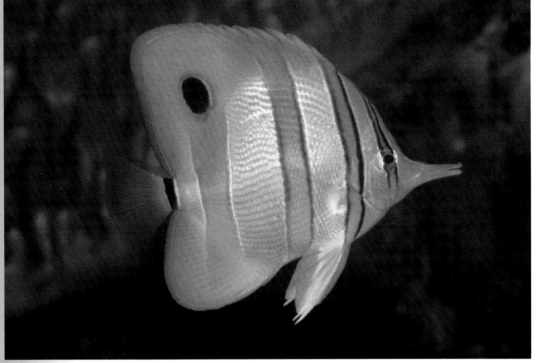

Habitat Coastal and inner reefs, often in turbid water, occasionally in estuaries. Depth ranges from 1-25 m.

Characters Prominent elongated snout; silvery-white ground color with three yellow-orange bars on sides (anterior-most bars with darkened edges); dark-edged orange bar through eye; ocellus on soft dorsal fin; soft dorsal and anal fins yellow-orange with blue submarginal band; dark bar across tail base. Juvenile almost identical to adult except all body bars have prominent dark edges. Maximum size about 20 cm. Juvenile similar to that of *Chelmon marginalis* (opposite), but has a wider midbody bar.

Remarks A territorial species which occurs either singly or in pairs. The elongated snout is an adaptation for feeding on benthic invertebrates in small crevices. A commonly encountered species on coastal reefs.

Distribution Throughout the Indo-Australian Archipelago, from the Andaman Sea to northwest Western Australia and the Great Barrier Reef, ranging northwards to the Ryukyu Islands.

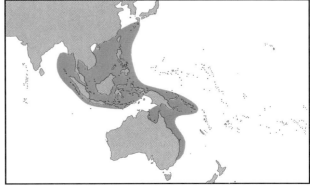

176

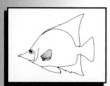

Chelmonops truncatus
Eastern Talma
(Kner 1859)

Rudie Kuiter

Habitat Coastal bays and estuaries, often adjacent to deep rocky walls, from 10-70 m.

Characters Silvery-white with three dark bars on sides; fourth dark bar through eye and brown stripe on middle of snout; rear edge of dorsal and anal fins convex, black in color, not prominently elongated at tips; reddish-brown bar just in front of rear edge of body; dark bar on tail base. Juvenile with ocellus on soft dorsal fin. Reaches maximum size of 22 cm. Very similar to *Chelmonops curiosus* (opposite), which differs in having a concave rear edge of the dorsal and anal fins which are also elongated at the tips.

Remarks Adults usually in pairs, juveniles solitary. Feeds on small crustaceans, worms, and filamentous algae. Juvenile retains ocellus until almost adult size.

Distribution Temperate coastal waters of southeastern Australia from southern Queensland to Jervis Bay.

Chelmonops curiosus
Western Talma
Kuiter 1986

Rudie Kuiter

Habitat Coastal rocky reefs, particularly on vertical rock faces, to a depth of at least 60 m.

Characters Silvery-white with three broad dark bars on sides; interiors of scales between bars brownish; dark bar through eye and dark stripe down middle of snout; rear margin of dorsal and anal fins black, concave, with corners of these fins slightly elongated; reddish-brown bar posterior to third body bar; dark bar on caudal-fin base. Juvenile similar to adult, but has ocellus on soft dorsal fin. Attains 26 cm. *Chelmonops truncatus* (opposite) is very similar, but best distinguished by rounded, convex rear margins of dorsal and anal fins (not prominently elongated at the tip as in *C. curiosus*).

Remarks Adults generally occur in pairs, juveniles are solitary. Juveniles lose ocellus at length of about 7.5 cm. Diet comprised of small worms, crustaceans, and algae. Specific name refers to the curious nature of this fish in relation to divers. It usually approaches very closely without any sign of fear. A recently described species formerly considered the same as *C. truncatus*.

Distribution Temperate coastal waters of southwestern and southern Australia, from Shark Bay to Adelaide.

178

Coradion altivelis
Highfin Coralfish
McCulloch 1916

Roger Steene

Habitat Inshore reefs with live coral cover as well as silty areas, in relatively shallow water (3-15 m).

Characters Soft dorsal and anal fins rounded and prominently elevated; silvery-white ground color with two closely spaced dark brown bars behind pectoral fins and third yellow-orange bar at rear of body extending onto adjacent fins; dark brown bar through eye; black bar across caudal-fin base. Juvenile same as adult, but posterior-most bar is brown and there is ocellus on soft dorsal fin. To 15 cm. Resembles *Coradion chrysozonus* (opposite), but adults of that species retain ocellus on the soft dorsal fin. Juveniles of the two species are virtually indistinguishable.

Remarks Usually uncommon throughout its range.

Distribution Indo-Australian Archipelago from the Andaman Sea to northwestern Australia and the Great Barrier Reef, extending northward to southern Japan.

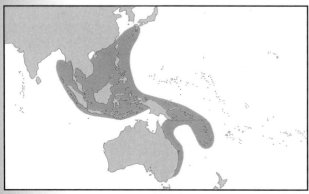

Coradion chrysozonus
Orange-Banded Coralfish
(Cuvier 1831)

Roger Steene

Habitat Usually found on coastal reefs, sometimes among rocks or over rubble where coral growth is relatively sparse. Ranges in depth from 3-60 m.

Characters Silvery-white with three brownish-orange bars on side, first two closely spaced, joining at base, third near rear edge of body extending onto adjacent fins; dark brown bar through eye; dark brown pelvic fins; oval-shaped black marking on caudal-fin base; small ocellus at base of soft dorsal fin (distinguishes adults of this species from *Coradion altivelis*, opposite). Juveniles similar to adults, but have proportionally larger ocellus. Grows to maximum size of 15 cm.

Remarks Occurs solitary or paired and is most abundant in relatively deep water and cooler areas exposed to upwelling. Diet consists mainly of sponges and tiny invertebrates which live on the sponge's surface.

Distribution Indo-Australian Archipelago and western Pacific region, from Thailand to the Solomon Islands, north to the Ryukyu and Bonin Island groups, and south to tropical Australian waters.

Coradion melanopus
Two-Eyed Coralfish
(Cuvier 1831)

Habitat   Coastal reefs, lagoons, and outer reef slopes, especially where barrel sponges abound, from about 10 to at least 30 m depth.

Characters   Two ocelli, one on soft dorsal fin, second on anal fin (sometimes less distinct); silvery-white ground color with three bars on sides, anterior-most bars brown and joined at base, and hind bar dusky gray with orange edges; dark brown bar through eye; dark pelvic fins. Reaches maximum size of 15 cm.

Remarks   A wary species, usually occurring in pairs. Feeds on barrel sponges and their resident invertebrate populations. Specific name translates to black (*melano-*) foot (*-pus*) in reference to the black pelvic fins.

Distribution   Restricted to southeast Asian waters, from Bali to Papua New Guinea, north to the Philippines.

Parachaetodon ocellatus
Ocellated Coralfish
(Cuvier 1831)

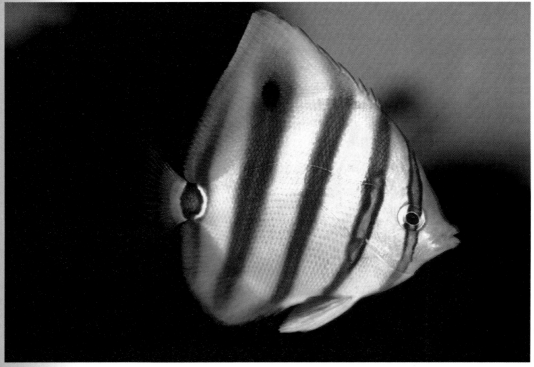

Roger Steene

Habitat   Coastal and inner reefs, often in sandy or silty flat-bottom areas littered with sponge growth. Sometimes found among seagrass.

Characters   Elevated, triangular dorsal fin, mostly yellowish; white ground color with series of four brownish-orange bars on sides; black-edged orange bar through eye; black spot on bar directly beneath apex of dorsal fin; black oval-shaped marking on base of tail with silver anterior edge (ocellus in juveniles). Maximum size about 18 cm.

Remarks   Generally occurs in pairs. The genus *Parachaetodon* is monotypic (i.e. contains a single species). Feeds on small benthic invertebrates and possibly sponges.

Distribution   Indo-west Pacific region, from India and Sri Lanka to Fiji, northwards to the Ryukyu and Bonin Islands, and southwards to New South Wales and Western Australia.

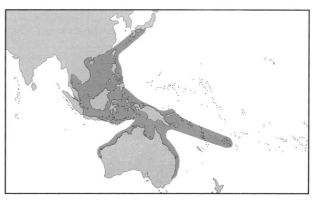

182

Forcipiger flavissimus
Forcepsfish
Jordan & McGregor 1898

Roger Steene

Habitat Exposed outer slopes with abundant coral growth and caves and ledges, from 2-114 m. Occasionally inhabiting coastal reefs and lagoons.

Characters Bright yellow body and median fins; upper section of head black, lower section silvery-white; black spot on anal fin just below tail base; mouth has small gape. Maximum size about 22 cm. Very similar to the closely related *F. longirostris* (opposite). Profile of the gill cover (rounded in this species, angular in *F. longirostris*) and the shorter snout length provide the best means of separation.

Remarks Usually occurs in pairs, but also solitary or in small groups. Preferred dietary items include pieces of larger prey (e.g. pedicellaria of echinoderms, tentacles of polychaetes), which are snipped off the living animals. Hydroids, crustaceans and fish eggs also consumed.

Distribution The most widely distributed butterflyfish species, occurring throughout the Indian and Pacific Oceans. Red Sea to central America, northwards to southern Japan, and south to Lord Howe, Kermadec and Easter islands.

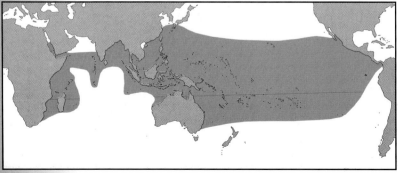

Forcipiger longirostris
Longnose Butterflyfish
(Broussonet 1782)

Roger Steene

Yellow form

Gerald R. Allen

Dark color form

Habitat Outer reef areas, often in the vicinity of drop-offs, from 5 to at least 60 m.

Characters Very elongate snout, mouth with very small gape; bright yellow body; upper section of head black, lower section silvery-white; small black spot below caudal-fin base; blue rear margin of dorsal and anal fins; transparent caudal fin. Some individuals (usually from around high, often volcanic islands) are entirely dark brown. Maximum size about 22 cm. Very similar to *Forcipiger flavissimus* (opposite), but has longer snout, more angular profile of gill cover, and virtually no mouth gape. Also distinguished by horizontal rows of small black spots on breast.

Remarks Uncommon in most areas, occurring alone or in pairs. Diet composed mostly of small invertebrates. Dark color phase (noted above) infrequently sighted.

Distribution Widespread through the Indo-west and central Pacific, from East Africa to Polynesia (including Hawaiian Is., Marquesas, Pitcairn I.). Northern limit of the range is the Ryukyu Islands, southern limit is tropical Australian waters.

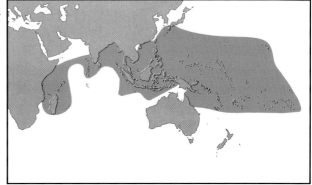

Hemitaurichthys multispinosus
Many-Spined Butterflyfish
Randall 1975

John E. Randall

Habitat Deep seaward reef slopes, to 50 m depth.

Characters Uniform gray body and fins; relatively elongate in shape. Grows to maximum size of about 20 cm. Similar in appearance to *Hemitaurichthys thompsoni* (opposite), but that species typically has more projecting snout profile; shorter snout of *H. multispinosus* superficially resembles that of a surgeonfish (Acanthuridae). The specific name alludes to its high number of dorsal spines (15 or 16) compared with other members of the genus.

Remarks A unique species in terms of the unusually high dorsal spine count and the peculiar elongate shape. Burgess (1978) suggested these characters warrant its placement in a separate subgenus: *Acanthotaurichthys*. There is little information on aspects of the life history.

Distribution Known only from Pitcairn Island in the southeastern Pacific Ocean.

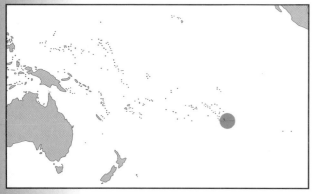

Hemitaurichthys thompsoni
Thompson's Butterflyfish
Fowler 1923

Gerald R. Allen

Habitat   Generally deep outer reef areas, from 10-300 m depth, but sometimes occurring in shallow lagoons and coastal reefs adjacent to deep water.

Characters   Uniform dark gray to nearly black on body and fins, lacks distinguishing marks. Reaches maximum size of 18 cm. Similar in appearance to *Hemitaurichthys multispinosus* (opposite), but that species has more elongate body and relatively short snout profile.

Remarks   A plankton-feeding fish that forms mid-water shoals. Pairs, solitary individuals and small groups are sometimes encountered in shallower water. Uusally not afraid of divers and can be approached at close range.

Distribution   Known from a number of islands and island groups in the central Pacific including the Marianas, Samoan Group, Hawaiian Islands, Johnston Atoll, Line Islands, and Tuamotu Islands.

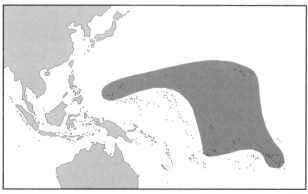

Hemitaurichthys polylepis
Pyramid Butterflyfish
(Bleeker 1857)

Roger Steene

Habitat	Outer reef slopes exposed to currents, particularly abundant in the vicinity of drop-offs, from 3-60 m.
Characters	White ground color distinctly forming pyramid shape between two sections of yellow on the upper corners of the body; entire dorsal fin and anal fin yellow; head black; pelvic, pectoral and caudal fins white. Attains 18 cm.
Remarks	Forms large shoals containing up to several hundred individuals in some areas. Feeds high in the water column on zooplankton. Large feeding shoals are a spectacular sight in clear oceanic waters. Areas exposed to strong currents are preferred as these conditions provide an abundant food supply.
Distribution	Throughout the central and western Pacific, from Southeast Asia to Polynesia (including Hawaiian Is. and Pitcairn), northwards to southern Japan and south to New Caledonia. Also occurs at Christmas Island and Cocos-Keeling Atoll in the eastern Indian Ocean.

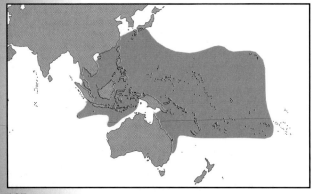

Hemitaurichthys zoster
Black Pyramid Butterflyfish
(Bennett 1831)

Habitat Outer reef slopes exposed to currents, ranging in depth from 1 to at least 35 m.

Characters Central portion of body white, broader at base; entire rear section of body and adjacent fins dark brown; head, breast and dorsal fin origin also dark brown; section of dorsal fin above white part of body yellowish; pectoral, pelvic and caudal fins white. Maximum size approximately 16 cm. Closely related to *H. polylepis* (opposite) from the western and central Pacific.

Remarks A planktivorous species that forms large aggregations numbering up to several hundred individuals. The shoal swims in mid-water along the upper edge of outer reef slopes, but is quick to retreat to the shelter of the reef surface when threatened.

Distribution Occurs throughout the Indian Ocean from coastal East Africa to the Andaman Sea. Southern limit of distribution is Mauritius and northern limit is coastal India.

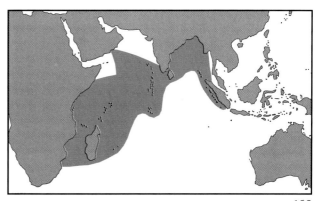

188

Heniochus acuminatus
Long-Fin Bannerfish
(Linnaeus 1758)

★ ★ ★

Gerald R. Allen

Habitat Lagoons and outer reef slopes, from 2-75 m, usually below 10 m. Inhabits shallower water in protected reef areas.

Characters Very elongate white dorsal filament; ground color white with two broad black bands on sides extending onto adjacent fins; pectoral, soft dorsal and caudal fins yellowish; pelvic fins black; black marks above eye and top of snout. Attains 25 cm. Nearly identical to *Heniochus diphreutes* (opposite), which has more rounded breast, less protruding snout, and its second black band ends at corner of the anal fin (ends just behind corner in *H. acuminatus*).

Remarks Adults occur alone, in pairs or sometimes in small groups, almost always swimming close to the reef . Feeds mostly on plankton, but supplements the diet with benthic invertebrates. Juveniles are solitary and have been observed picking parasites from other fishes.

Distribution Widespread through the Indo-west and central Pacific, from East Africa and the Arabian Gulf to the Society Islands, north to southern Japan and south to Lord Howe Island.

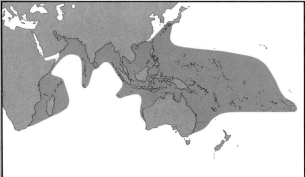

Heniochus diphreutes
Schooling Bannerfish
Jordan 1903

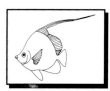

Habitat Generally on deep outer reef slopes, from 5-210 m, but usually below 15 m. Inhabits shallower water in cool upwelling areas in the tropics.

Characters Elongate white dorsal filament; ground color white with two broad black bands on sides, extending onto adjacent fins; pectoral, soft dorsal and caudal fins yellowish; pelvic fins black; dark marks above eye and top of snout. Attains 21 cm. Nearly identical to *Heniochus acuminatus* (opposite), but has more rounded breast, less protruding snout, and its second black band ends at corner of anal fin (ends just behind the corner in *H. acuminatus*).

Remarks Both adults and juveniles are usually encountered in shoals, whereas *H. acuminatus* is generally found alone or in pairs (rarely in groups), which is a practical way of distinguishing the two. Unlike *H. acuminatus*, which tends to swim close to the reef, it swims up to several meters off the bottom while feeding on zooplankton. Juveniles have been observed cleaning parasites from other fishes.

Distribution Widely distributed throughout the Indo-west and central Pacific, from the Red Sea and coast of East Africa to the western Pacific rim: southern Japan to New South Wales and Kermadec Island. Also found at the Hawaiian Islands. More common at subtropical localities.

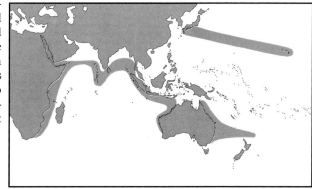

Heniochus chrysostomus
Pennant Bannerfish
Cuvier 1831

Roger Steene

Habitat Areas of prolific coral growth including coastal reefs, lagoons and on outer reefs, to 45 m depth, but usually in less than 15 m.

Characters Tallest dorsal spine elongated into feather-shaped pennant; white ground color with black band across head, just encompassing eye; pair of additional lighter brown bands more posterior on body; pelvic fins black; snout yellow. Reaches maximum size of 18 cm.

Remarks Solitary individuals most often encountered, but pairs or small groups sometimes seen. Often found in vicinity of *Heniochus varius* (page 196). Coral polyps constitute the bulk of the diet. Juveniles are common in shallow areas with coral and algal cover.

Distribution Mainly western Pacific region, from Western Australia to Pitcairn Island, north to southern Japan and south as far as New Caledonia.

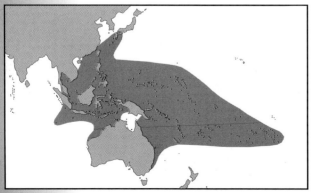

Heniochus intermedius
Red Sea Bannerfish
Steindachner 1893

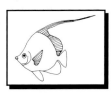

Roger Steene

Habitat Coral reefs, from 3-50 m depth.

Characters Elongate white dorsal filament; ground color white suffused with yellow; two black bands on sides, anterior-most passing just behind the head and encompassing eye; soft dorsal, pectoral, anal, and caudal fins yellow; pelvic fins black. Reaches maximum size of 18 cm. Similar in appearance to both *Heniochus acuminatus* (page 189) and *H. diphreutes* (page 190), but readily distinguished from these species by its more yellowish ground color and placement of the first black band next to the eye.

Remarks Most often encountered alone or in pairs, but large aggregations are also found. Juveniles may form large aggregations, sometimes mixed with *H. diphreutes*, especially in deep reef areas where corals are sparse. Diet includes zooplankton and benthic invertebrates.

Distribution Restricted to the Red Sea (common in the Gulf of Aqaba) and adjacent Gulf of Aden.

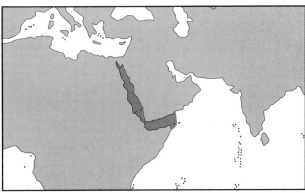

192

Heniochus monoceros
Masked Bannerfish
Cuvier 1831

★ ★ ★

Roger Steene

Habitat Areas of prolific coral growth including lagoons and outer reefs, ranging in depth from 2-25 m but usually below 15 m.

Characters Face black with pale stripes between eyes and on forehead, becoming brownish on forehead; white ground color with central broad black band tapering dorsally, and second broad dark band on rear part of body; dorsal, caudal and most of anal fin yellow; pelvic fins black; elongate, but relatively short dorsal fin filament. Attains 23 cm. *Heniochus singularius* (opposite) is similar, but has white nape (not brown as in this species), and central black band passes in front of dorsal filament (not behind as in *H. monoceros*).

Remarks Adults occur alone, in pairs or in small shoals, juveniles are solitary. Feeds on benthic invertebrates such as polychaete worms. A shy and relatively uncommon species.

Distribution Wide ranging throughout the Indo-west and central Pacific, from East Africa to the Tuamotu Islands. Northern limit of range is southern Japan, southern limit is Lord Howe Island.

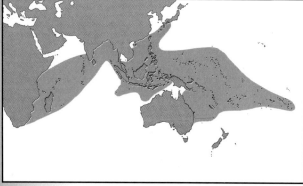

Heniochus singularius
Singular Bannerfish
Smith & Radcliffe 1911

Roger Steene

Habitat Coastal, inner and outer reef slopes, from 2-50 m depth. Also frequently sighted on shipwrecks. Juveniles usually in shallow lagoons but also in deep water around caves and other refuges.

Characters Two black bands on sides, their inner edges fading to central white band with dark scale centers; shortened white dorsal filament; remainder of dorsal fin and caudal fin yellow; dark bar through eye and another encircling snout, separated by white bar; black hump on nape; black pelvic fins. Reaches 25 cm length. Similar to *Heniochus monoceros* (opposite), but is easily distinguished by the position of the central dark bar (passing in front of dorsal filament in this species, and behind it in *H. monoceros*) and lack of yellow coloration on anal fin.

Remarks A relatively shy species occurring alone or in pairs. Diet is comprised of coral polyps, benthic invertebrates and algae.

Distribution Widely distributed in the Indo-west and central Pacific, from the Maldives to Samoa. North to southern Japan and south to New Caledonia.

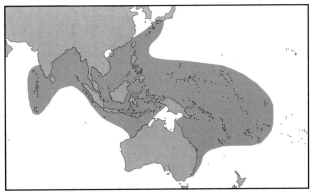

Heniochus pleurotaenia
Phantom Bannerfish
Ahl 1923

★ ★ ★

Gerald R. Allen

Habitat Areas of rich coral growth, from 1-25 m depth.

Characters Two horn-like bony projections on head at level of eye, and hump on nape; white ground color, with two broad black bands on lower sides, becoming pale brown and converging dorsally; front edge of head and nape to eye dark brown; soft dorsal fin pale brown; anal and pelvic fins black; lacks elongate dorsal filament. Reaches maximum size of 17 cm. Resembles *Heniochus varius* (opposite), but that species almost entirely dark brown, lacking central white marking.

Remarks Occurring solitary, paired, or in aggregations of up to 20-30 individuals. This species sometimes exhibits territorial behavior with individuals pushing out encroaching conspecifics using their forehead. The humps on the forehead possibly represent an adaptation suited for this aggressive behavior.

Distribution Northeastern Indian Ocean, from the Maldives and Sri Lanka to Java and the Andaman Sea.

Heniochus varius
Humphead Bannerfish
(Cuvier 1829)

Gerald R. Allen

Habitat   Areas of rich coral growth in lagoons and on seaward slopes, ranging in depth between 2-30 m. Prefers the shelter of caves or ledges rather than open terrain.

Characters   Dark brown head with two horn-like bony protuberances at level of eyes, and another protuberance on forehead; most of body and fins dark brown, becoming paler brown dorsally; narrow white band behind head to breast, and diagonal white band extending from the middle of dorsal fin to base of tail. Juvenile lacks humps on the head and has more elongate dorsal spines than adult. Reaches maximum size of 19 cm. Vaguely resembles *Heniochus pleurotaenia* (opposite), but that species distinguished by a central white patch on the body.

Remarks   An intrepid species, unafraid of approaching divers. Occurs alone, paired, or in aggregations numbering up to 30 individuals. Diet consists of coral polyps and other reef invertebrates.

Distribution   Western and central Pacific Ocean, from Southeast Asia to the Society Islands, northwards to southern Japan and south to New Caledonia.

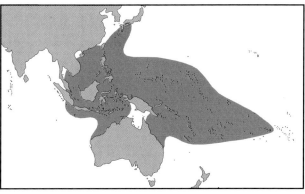

Prognathodes guezei
Gueze's Butterflyfish
Maugé & Bauchot 1976

Jill Ruse

Habitat Deep reef areas below 80 m. Most common at depths of about 100 m.

Characters White overall with two broad black bars on sides extending onto dorsal fin; narrower black bar from dorsal fin origin, through eye, to snout; darkened rear margin of dorsal and anal fins, and black bar across tail base. Reaches maximum size of about 11 cm.

Remarks The only observations of living specimens were made using a deep-diving submersible. Prior to this, the species was known only on the basis of dead specimens captured in deep traps. Just prior to publication of this book, Richard Pyle informed us that he has collected a new species similar to *P. guezei*. It is apparently confined to deep waters of the Hawaiian Islands down to at least 120 m.

Distribution Known only from the western Indian Ocean at the Comoro Islands, Réunion, and Mauritius.

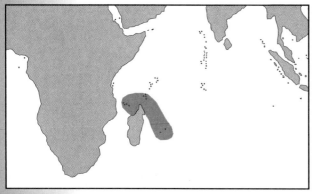

Prognathodes guyotensis
Guyote Butterflyfish
Yamamoto & Tameka 1982

Jill Ruse

Habitat Oceanic seamounts, usually in extremely deep water (100-300 m).

Characters Pale yellowish with broad black band from just behind dorsal fin origin to anal fin; dusky brown to black markings on nape and forehead to below eye and top of snout; pelvic fins black. Maximum size about 13 cm.

Remarks Discovered by Japanese government research vessel engaged in deep-sea trawling operations in 1978. Collected at 320 m, the deepest recorded occurrence of any butterflyfish species. More recently it has been captured from the Maldive Islands. Closely related to *Prognathodes guezei* (opposite), an inhabitant of deep reefs in the Western Indian Ocean. Specific name is derived from the word guyote: a geographical term meaning submerged flat-top mountain; referring to the habitat.

Distribution Central Indian Ocean at the Maldive Islands and northwestern Pacific region, along the Palau-Kyushu Ridge.

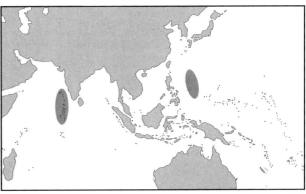

CHAPTER 4

THE EASTERN PACIFIC-ATLANTIC REGION

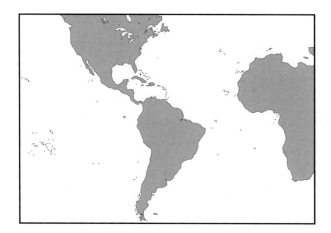

Although seemingly isolated from each other, the tropical reef faunas of the Atlantic and eastern Pacific have far more in common than either has with the fauna of the vast Indo-west Pacific. This is because the two regions were continuous until uplifting of the Central American land bridge closed the gap, probably in the early Pliocene epoch (roughly five million years ago). Species diversity is extremely poor compared to the Indo-west Pacific. Only 30 species (13 angelfishes and 17 butterflyfishes) are found in the region. Nearly half of these inhabit the Caribbean Sea or West Indies. The most impoverished area lies along the west coast of Africa where only three species are known. Due to cold currents and upwelling the tropical zone in the eastern Pacific is much contracted, which is a contributing factor in its lower number of species compared to the Caribbean. Four angelfishes and five butterflyfishes occur in the region. One of these, the Forcepsfish (*Forcipiger flavissimus*), has a broad distribution mainly covering the Indo-west Pacific (see page 183). In addition, the butterflyfishes *Chaetodon auriga* (page 97), *C. kleinii* (page 159), and *C. lunula* (page 142) are Indo-west Pacific "vagrants" infrequently found at the Galapagos.

Reference List for Angelfishes and Butterflyfishes of the E. Pacific-Atlantic Region

Opposite: Golfito Bay on Costa Rica's western coast (Photo by Gerald R. Allen).

Centropyge argi
Cherubfish
Woods & Kanazawa 1951

Helmut Debelius/Ikan

Habitat Coral reefs and rubble bottoms usually below 30 m depth. Occasionally observed in shallower water (5-10 m).

Characters Deep blue body with yellow or orange face; blue ring around eye. Juvenile similar to adult, but facial coloration less defined. *Centropyge aurantonota* (opposite) is similar in appearance, but yellow coloration extends above the eye in this species. Maximum size 6.5 cm.

Remarks Although first collected in 1908, this species was not scientifically described until 1951 when it was "rediscovered" in a museum collection. Most commonly observed darting in and out of reef crevices.

Distribution Bermuda, West Indies and southern parts of the Gulf of Mexico.

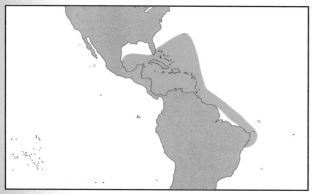

Centropyge aurantonota
Flameback Pygmy Angelfish
Burgess 1974

Habitat Isolated patches of staghorn coral (*Acropora cervicornis*) and rubble areas at depths ranging from 16 to below 200 m. Most commonly observed from 16-25 m.

Characters Similar markings to *Centropyge argi* (opposite) however, yellow-orange head coloration extends to beginning of the dorsal fin in adults, and to rear part of dorsal fin in juveniles. Attains maximum size of 6 cm.

Remarks The first specimens of *C. aurantonota* were discovered by aquarium fish collectors at Barbados and Curacao. The specific name refers to the orange (*aurant-*) back (*-nota*) of juveniles and sub-adults.

Distribution Southern portion of the Caribbean Sea (including the Lesser Antilles, Curacao, Barbados, and St. Lucia) to Brazil.

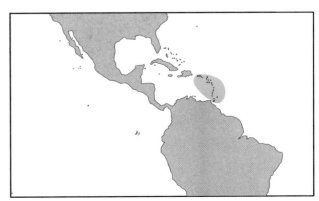

Centropyge resplendens
Resplendent Pygmy Angelfish
Lubbock & Sankey 1975

Helmut Debelius/Ikan

Habitat Rock and rubble bottoms at depths between 15-40 m.

Characters Yellow-orange color extending from mouth along upper back and encompassing dorsal fin; caudal fin also yellow-orange; fin margins blue, same color as body. Females distinguished from males on basis of anal fin color, which is more yellow in males. Reaches maximum size of 6 cm.

Remarks *C. resplendens* bears a remarkable resemblance to the western Pacific damselfish *Chrysiptera starcki*, an example of evolutionary convergence, whereby two unrelated organisms share similar color patterns and/or morphological characteristics. *C. resplendens* is closely related to the other tropical Atlantic representatives of the genus: *C. argi* (page 201) and *C. aurantonotus* (page 202), but does not have as much yellow-orange on the head.

Distribution Found only on remote Ascension Island in the central Atlantic Ocean.

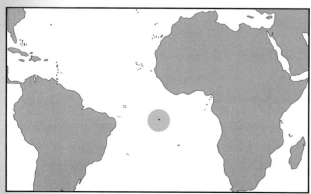

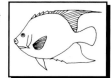

Holacanthus africanus
West African Angelfish
Cadenat 1950

Helmut Debelius/Ikan

Juvenile

Helmut Debelius/Ikan

Sub-adult

Helmut Debelius/Ikan

Adult

Habitat   Usually found among rocks at depths from 0.3 m (surge zone) to at least 45 m.

Characters   Adult: Mostly brown or olive green with paler rear half of body and dark area in front of tail; prominent black spot above pectoral fin. Juvenile: Mainly dark brown with bluish dorsal and anal fins, yellow tail, and bluish-white bar across middle of body. Sub-adults have orange on outer portion of dorsal and anal fins, and midbody bar is broader and white in color. Maximum size attained 45 cm.

Remarks   Found on rocky reefs with patchy coral cover. At Isla Principe in the Gulf of Guinea, it is relatively abundant, with about 30 fish per 100 square metres of rocky bottom. Juveniles are abundant during June and July and are very aggressive towards one another. Both adults and juveniles are easy to approach. Seldom seen in captivity, which is true of most fishes from the tropical eastern Atlantic.

Distribution   Tropical west African coast between Senegal and the Congo. Relatively common off the coast of Ghana.

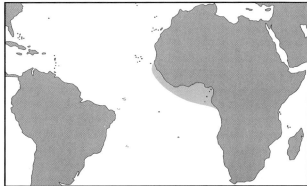

Holacanthus bermudensis
Blue Angelfish
Goode 1876

Kiyoshi Endoh

Kiyoshi Endoh

Habitat Coral reefs and rocky areas from 2 m to below 92 m depth. Juveniles more common in channels and on inshore reefs in shallow water.

Characters Adult: Rear edge of fin margins yellow; throat and base of pectoral fins blue. Juvenile: Dark overall with series of narrow blue bars across body. Juvenile very similar to *Holacanthus ciliaris* (opposite), but distinguished by straight bars in middle of body compared to curved markings of *H. ciliaris*. Maximum length approximately 38 cm.

Remarks Closely related to *H. ciliaris* and hybrids of these two species are not uncommon where distributions overlap (e.g. Florida and Bahamas). Hybrids may have distinctive markings of either or both species.

Distribution East coast of North America (North Carolina to southern Florida), Bahamas, Bermuda, and Gulf of Mexico (Yucatan to western and northern offshore banks).

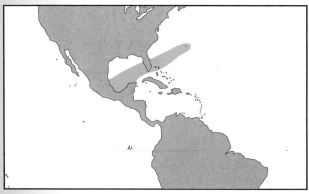

Holacanthus ciliaris
Queen Angelfish
(Linnaeus 1758)

Roger Steene

Habitat   Offshore reefs among sea whips, sea fans, and hard corals at depths between 2 m and at least 70 m.

Characters   Adult: Cheeks, caudal, pelvic and pectoral fins orange; blue-ringed, dark ocellated spot on forehead with blue speckles ("crown"). Juveniles: Similar to juvenile of *Holacanthus bermudensis* (opposite), but midbody bars curved instead of straight; also body shape more triangular than that of *H. bermudensis*. Grows to maximum size of 45 cm.

Remarks   Found solitary or in pairs. Adults feed primarily on sponges as well as algae, hydroids, tunicates and bryozoans. Juveniles occasionally clean ectoparasites from other fishes. Hybridizes with the closely related *H. bermudensis*. Island populations (i.e. Caribbean, Bahamas, Bermuda) more brightly colored than those from coastal areas. Color variations not uncommon; individuals may have an overall yellow or green appearance rather than that illustrated here.

Distribution   Tropical western Atlantic from Brazil to Florida and the Bahamas. Also found in the Gulf of Mexico.

206

Holacanthus limbaughi
Clipperton Angelfish
Baldwin 1963

Gerald R. Allen

Habitat   Inhabits relatively steep outer reef slopes, most commonly in 10-20 m, but ranges deeper, to at least 40 m.

Characters   Adult: Overall dark blue-gray with white caudal fin and small white spot above tip of pectoral fin. Juvenile: Dark gray with seven narrow vertical bluish bars on side. To at least 24 cm.

Remarks   About 10-15 individuals seen on each dive, usually as solitary individuals. Juveniles relatively uncommon (April), sheltering in boulder crevices.

Distribution   Found only on Clipperton Island in the eastern Pacific Ocean, approximately 1200 km southwest of Acapulco, Mexico and 2,000 km northwest of the Galapagos. Tiny Clipperton is the only true coral atoll in the eastern Pacific. A narrow ring of land completely encloses a central freshwater lagoon. The total area of land and lagoon occupies less than 10 square kilometers.

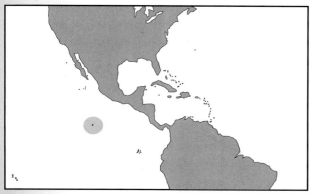

Holacanthus passer
King Angelfish
Valenciennes 1846

Roger Steene

Adult

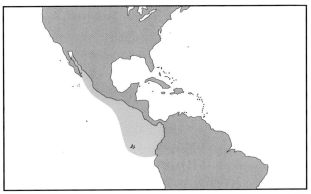

Juvenile

Gerald R. Allen

Habitat Most common on rocky reefs, but sometimes found in coral areas at depths from 3 to at least 80 m, usually in clear water. Juveniles hide in reef crevices and seldom venture far from cover, or may occur in tide pools.

Characters Adult: Dark blue-gray with white bar extending from dorsal fin to pectoral fin level, tapering at bottom; orange-yellow fan-shaped tail. Juvenile: Brown and orange body with similar markings to those of *Holacanthus clarionensis* (page 209), but generally darker; narrow blue bar behind eye extends to below cheek spine (ends at spine in *H. clarionensis*). Maximum size about 25 cm.

Remarks Occurs solitary, in pairs (usually during breeding season in late summer), or in aggregations. Females defend territories aggressively during breeding season. Usually wary of divers and difficult to approach. Sometimes forms mixed aggregations with *Pomacanthus zonipectus* (page 213). Diet includes algae, plankton, sponges and other invertebrates. Juveniles sometimes clean ectoparasites from other fish.

Distribution Tropical eastern Pacific including Gulf of California (central and southern parts) to Ecuador and the Galapagos Islands.

208

Holacanthus clarionensis
Clarion Angelfish
Gilbert 1890

Ross Robertson

Juvenile

Ross Robertson

Adult

Habitat Rocky reefs and coral areas, usually between 10-30 m.

Characters Adult: Brownish on head; most of body with wide orange-yellow region just behind head; dorsal and anal fin margins deep blue. Juvenile: Similar ground color, but with series of white bars with deep blue margins on side and across head; tail and margins of fins same color as adult. Bars on side become narrower with increased growth until they finally disappear. Maximum size 20 cm.

Remarks Juveniles have similar markings to those of *Holacanthus passer* (page 208), but body not as dark overall, and more distinctively orange. Generally found solitary or in large grazing aggregations.

Distribution Common at Clarion and other islands of the Revillagigedos Group, and to a lesser extent at Clipperton Island off the central American coast in the eastern Pacific. Also recorded from the southern tip of Baja California where it is far less common.

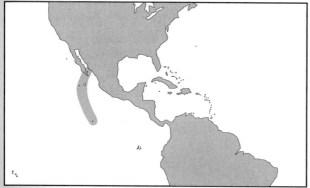

Holacanthus tricolor
Rock Beauty
(Bloch 1795)

Juvenile

Adonal

John E. Randall

Adult

John E. Randall

Habitat Rock-rubble areas, and coral reefs from 1 to below 90 m. Particularly common on seaward facing reefs and on shallow reefs with abundant coral growth. Juveniles commonly associated with *Millepora* fire corals.

Characters Adult: Yellow head, anterior portion of the body, and tail; lips navy blue; rest of body black. Juvenile: Entirely yellow with ocellated black spot (with blue margin) on side - this spot enlarges with maturation and eventually forms dark patch covering entire posterior section of body. Maximum size 30 cm.

Remarks The most common angelfish on tropical western Atlantic reefs. Juveniles resemble the damselfish *Stegastes planifrons* (also occurs in the range occupied by *H. tricolor*), but can be distinguished by a more rounded body shape and the absence of a small black spot on top of the caudal-fin base. Individuals from offshore island populations are generally more colorful than coastal fish.

Distribution Extensive distribution in tropical western Atlantic from Georgia (North America) to Bermuda, and northern Gulf of Mexico to Brazil.

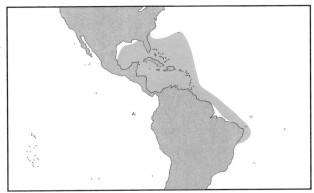

Pomacanthus arcuatus
Gray Angelfish
(Linnaeus 1758)

Roger Steene

Habitat   Reef areas with rich coral growth, most commonly between 2-30 m.

Characters   Adult: Light gray with darker scale centers giving spotted appearance; dorsal and anal fins broad, ending in filaments; caudal fin truncate. Juvenile: Triangle-shaped body with five yellow bars on side; almost identical to juvenile of *Pomacanthus paru* (opposite), but has narrower black bar on caudal fin. Intermediate color patterns observed in sub-adults (up to 25 cm) with overall gray color of adult and remnant pale bars of juvenile stage. A large angelfish, reaching maximum size of about 50 cm.

Remarks   Conspicuous member of the reef fauna due to its large size. Occurs solitary or in pairs. Diet consists mainly of sponges, but also feeds on wide variety of other items including corals, tunicates, bryozoans, seagrasses, and algae. A curious fish that will approach divers.

Distribution   Tropical western Atlantic from New York (North America) to the Bahamas, and from Gulf of Mexico to Brazil including the Caribbean. Also occurs at Bermuda where it has been introduced.

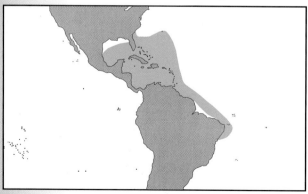

★ ★

Pomacanthus paru
French Angelfish
(Bloch 1787)

Adult

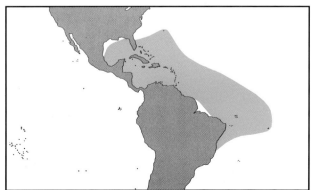

Juvenile

Habitat Rich coral areas and rocky reefs from 5 to 100 m.

Characters Adult: Similar overall body shape to *Pomacanthus arcuatus* (opposite), but caudal fin more rounded; dark body with yellow scale margins; head bluish, paler than body; yellow marking at base of pectoral fin; pale markings around mouth and in front of eye; dorsal filament lighter than rest of fin. Juvenile: Dark body with series of five yellow bars; very similar to *P. arcuatus* (opposite) but black caudal fin entirely surrounded by yellow margin. Reaches maximum size of 38 cm.

Remarks Often encountered in pairs near sea fans. Feeds on wide variety of reef fauna, focusing on sponges. Diet is similar to that of *P. arcuatus*. Juveniles supplement diet by cleaning ectoparasites from larger fish. The scientific name "*paru*" is derived from the traditional Brazilian name for the species. Like *P. arcuatus*, this species was originally described in the butterflyfish genus *Chaetodon*.

Distribution Florida coast to the Bahamas, and from northern Gulf of Mexico to Brazil. Also occurs at St. Paul's Rocks and Ascension Island in central tropical Atlantic. Introduced population exists at Bermuda. Vagrants reported from the Gulf of Guinea, in the eastern Atlantic.

Pomacanthus zonipectus
Cortez Angelfish
(Gill 1862)

Juvenile

Adult

Gerald R. Allen

Habitat Inhabits rocky reefs and coral areas. Most commonly observed on isolated reef patches surrounded by sand between 6-15 m depth, but depth range extends to at least 35 m.

Characters Adult: Dusky light gray, darkening on head and posterior parts; broad yellow bar behind head, and another narrower yellow bar between pair of dark bars just behind level of pectoral fin. Juvenile: Dark body with six yellow bands (arc-shaped posteriorly) and narrow blue bands between. Maximum size recorded about 48 cm.

Remarks Solitary and fiercely territorial as a juvenile (although shoals of juveniles have also been reported!), but commonly forms aggregations as an adult. Diet is similar to *Holacanthus passer* (page 208), being composed mostly of sponges, but algae, bryozoans, eggs, and tunicates are also consumed. Mixed aggregations of these two species occur presumably because their dietary preferences are similar. Juveniles clean parasites from other fish.

Distribution Widely distributed in the tropical eastern Pacific from Baja California and the Sea of Cortez to coastal Peru. Also occurs at offshore islands such as the Revillagigedos and Galapagos.

Amphichaetodon melbae
San Felix Butterflyfish
Burgess & Caldwell 1978

John E. Randall

Habitat Rocky reefs. Information on depth distribution is scant, but has been collected between 9-12 m.

Characters Pale ground color with series of five black bars on side (three on body, one on caudal-fin base, one through eye); black stripe on snout; dorsal, anal, and caudal fins yellow; pelvic fins with broad black margin. Morphologically similar to *Amphichaetodon howensis* (page 94) from the southwestern Pacific, but that species has much broader bars on the body. Reaches a maximum size of approximately 15 cm.

Remarks A little known species, due to its remote and restricted distribution. Water temperatures in its habitat are relatively cool, ranging from 16-19°C.

Distribution Known only from San Felix Island off the coast of Chile.

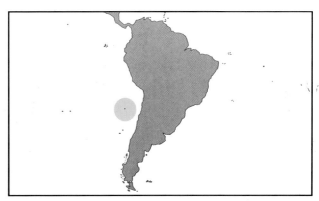

Chaetodon hoefleri
Hoefler's Butterflyfish
Steindachner 1883

R. Lubbock/Ikan

Habitat Coastal waters on mixed substrata including rock (with scattered coral growth), mud, and sand. Ranges in depth from 5-150 m, most common between 20-75 m.

Characters Silvery-white with yellow spots on scale centers; series of brown bars including one through eye, two broader bars on body, one across base of caudal fin, and one through middle of caudal fin; prominent black spot on upper part of second body bar; anal and pelvic fins yellowish, dorsal fin brownish yellow. Juvenile similar to adult. Maximum size approximately 20 cm.

Remarks Closely related to *Chaetodon marleyi* (page 152) of southeastern Africa, which is possibly only a subspecies of *C. hoefleri*. The two are geographically separated by about 15° of latitude and share nearly identical color patterns. The juvenile lacks the second dark spot on the dorsal fin that is typically seen in the young of *C. marleyi*.

Distribution Tropical west African coast from Mauritania to Angola.

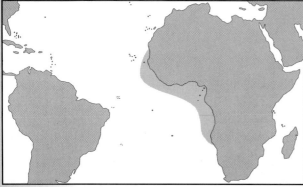

Chaetodon robustus
Robust or Ghana Butterflyfish
Günther 1860

Helmut Debelius/Ikan

Habitat   Rocky reefs with scattered coral patches, from 3 to at least 50 m depth.

Characters   Silvery white to pale yellowish; two widely spaced dark brown bars, becoming yellowish ventrally; black eye-bar and dark stripe on snout; pelvic fins yellow, soft portions of dorsal and anal fins brownish yellow; yellowish bar across base of white caudal fin. Juveniles similar to adult, but with two white-edged dark spots at front and rear of dorsal fin. Maximum size about 17 cm. Similar in appearance to *Chaetodon hoefleri* (opposite) from western Africa and *C. marleyi* (page 152) from southeastern Africa, but both of these species have a yellowish bar on the caudal fin.

Remarks   The most common butterflyfish along the tropical west African coast, usually encountered in pairs. Often found on the edge of rocky reefs where it forages on adjacent sand bottoms. Relatively common at Isla Sao Tome in the Gulf of Guinea. A relatively easy species to approach underwater.

Distribution   Tropical west African coast, particularly common in the northern Gulf of Guinea, also at the Cape Verde Islands.

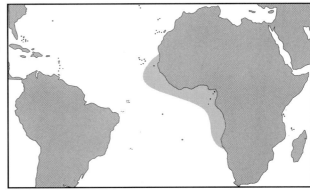

Chaetodon capistratus
Foureye Butterflyfish
Linnaeus 1758

Juvenile

Sub-adult

John E. Randall

Roger Steene

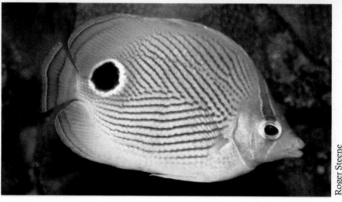

Adult

Roger Steene

Habitat Seaward and inner reefs rich in coral growth, from 2-20 m. Sometimes observed among sea grass.

Characters Adult: Ground color grayish-white with series of thin lines radiating diagonally above and below middle of body; large white-edged ocellus anterior to tail base; dark bar through eye. Juvenile: Ocellus same as adult (very small juveniles have a second ocellus on soft dorsal fin); two broad dark bars on body; dark bar through eye. Maximum size approximately 15 cm. Juveniles similar to those of *Chaetodon striatus* (page 219), but that species lacks a prominent ocellus in front of the tail base.

Remarks Type species of the genus *Chaetodon*. Most common butterflyfish in the Caribbean. Occurs solitary or paired, feeds on zoantharians, polychaetes, gorgonians, and tunicates. Usually easy to approach.

Distribution Coastal Venezuela through the Caribbean Sea, West Indies, and Gulf of Mexico to Florida. Also at Bermuda. Juvenile recruits stray up the east coast of USA as far as Massachusetts.

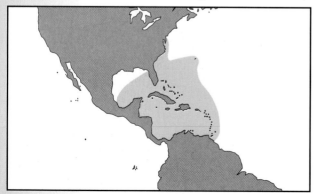

Chaetodon ocellatus
Spotfin Butterflyfish
Bloch 1781

Roger Steene

Habitat Coral reef habitats at depths between 3-28 m.

Characters Adult: Silvery-white with all fins yellow (except pectorals); bluish submarginal bands on caudal and anal fins; black bar through eye; small black spot on soft dorsal fin, sometimes faded; yellow markings on margin of gill cover and snout. Juvenile: Similar to adult but with black bar along posterior-most part of body and adjacent fins (fades with growth); caudal fin transparent. Reaches maximum size of 20 cm. Slight resemblance to juveniles of *Chaetodon sanctaehelenae* (page 222), but that species has a dark band on the anal fin.

Remarks Occurs solitary or paired. Dusky bands are apparent on the body at night.

Distribution Tropical western Atlantic Ocean, from Brazil to the Gulf of Mexico, throughout the Caribbean, also at Bermuda. Common on Florida reefs. Juveniles have been recorded as far north as Massachusetts and Nova Scotia, swept to these latitudes in the warm Gulf Stream during the summer.

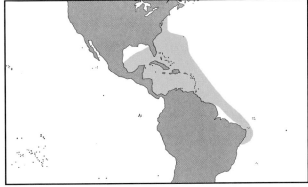

Chaetodon striatus
Banded Butterflyfish
Linnaeus 1758

Roger Steene

Habitat Rocky and coral covered reefs, from 3-20 m.

Characters Silvery-white with three broad brown bars on sides, the posterior-most bar along the rear edge of the body (missing in the similar *Chaetodon humeralis* from the eastern Pacific - opposite); broad submarginal brown bands on soft portions of median fins (including caudal fin); narrow brown bar through eye. Juveniles with an ocellated spot on soft dorsal fin, resembling those of sympatric *Chaetodon capistratus* (page 217), but rear section of the body is completely dark in that species. Maximum size about 17 cm.

Remarks Common throughout its distribution, occurring solitary or paired. Feeds on a variety of items, predominantly polychaetes and coral polyps, but also mollusc eggs and small crustaceans. Known to form hybrids with *Chaetodon ocellatus* (page 218).

Distribution Tropical western Atlantic, from Gulf of Mexico, throughout the West Indies to Brazil (including Fernando de Noronha). East to St. Paul's Rocks and northwards to Massachusetts (USA) where larvae are sometimes swept in warm Gulf Stream currents. Also recorded at Bermuda.

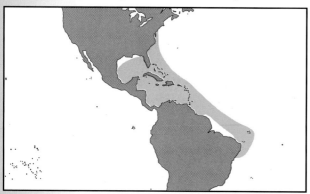

Chaetodon humeralis
East Pacific Butterflyfish
Günther 1860

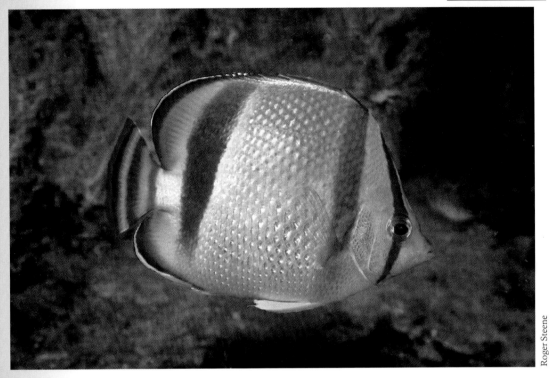

Roger Steene

Habitat   Shallow inshore rocky reefs and tide pools, occasionally on sand bottoms, usually from 3-12 m, but has been recorded as deep as 55 m. Inhabits areas where water temperatures are typically cool (18-19°C) due to oceanic upwelling.

Characters   Silvery white with three prominent brown to black bands, one through eye, and two widely spaced, broader bars on body; soft portions of dorsal and anal fins with dark submarginal bands and a silvery-white margin; caudal fin with alternating dark and light bands. Juvenile with ocellus on soft dorsal fin. Reaches a maximum size of about 18 cm. Similar in appearance to *Chaetodon striatus* (opposite) from the Caribbean, which has more closely spaced bars on the body.

Remarks   The most common butterflyfish in shallow waters of the tropical eastern Pacific. Occurs in pairs or small aggregations. Relatively easy to approach.

Distribution   Tropical eastern Pacific, from the Gulf of California (more common on mainland coast) to Peru, also at the Galapagos and other offshore islands.

Chaetodon sedentarius
Reef Butterflyfish
Poey 1860

John E. Randall

Habitat Coastal and offshore coral reefs, from 5-92 m. Most frequently encountered below 15 m.

Characters White becoming pale yellowish dorsally; bold black bar through eye; broad dark bar along rear edge of body and adjacent fins (dark pigmentation on soft dorsal fin fades with onset of maturity). Juvenile similar to adult but with a black spot on the soft dorsal fin. Reaches maximum size of about 15 cm.

Remarks Occurs mostly in pairs, but solitary individuals are also encountered. Feeds on a variety of benthic invertebrates including polychaete worms, small crustaceans, and hydroids. Inhabits slightly deeper water than other Caribbean *Chaetodon*.

Distribution Tropical western Atlantic, from the Gulf of Mexico, throughout the West Indies to Brazil. Range extends northwards along the east coast of North America to North Carolina.

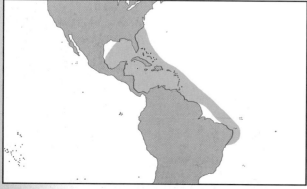

Chaetodon sanctaehelenae
St. Helena Butterflyfish
Günther 1868

Kiyoshi Endoh

Habitat Rocky areas, from 1 to at least 25 m depth.

Characters Silvery white with broad yellow-orange margin on median fins; yellowish to brown bar through eye, extending a short distance below eye; base of caudal fin yellow-orange, becoming transparent towards edge. Juvenile similar to adult, but with dark spot on soft dorsal fin, dark margin on anal fin, and slightly darker bar through eye. Attains 15 cm. Juveniles resemble *Chaetodon ocellatus* (page 218), but are distinguished by the dark marking on the anal fin.

Remarks Usually encountered in pairs, but large aggregations of up to several hundred individuals are sometimes encountered, for example near the sewage outlet at James Bay (St. Helena Island) and around wharves where anglers dispose of fish scraps. Forages on plankton in mid-water.

Distribution Previously known only from St. Helena and Ascension, two small islands in the tropical Atlantic Ocean. Recently sighted in the Canary Islands.

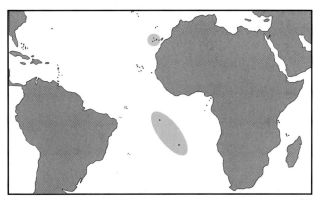

Johnrandallia nigrirostris
Barberfish
(Gill 1862)

Gerald R. Allen

Habitat	Rocky reefs and coral areas, between 6-40 m.
Characters	Silvery-yellow overall with a broad diagonal black band along upper rear edge of body to tail base; head silver with black markings on forehead, around eye, encircling snout, and on margin of gill cover. Adult are generally more silver overall than juvenile (<u>illustrated</u>). Reaches a maximum size of 20 cm.
Remarks	Occurring in small to large aggregations, this species provides a valuable ectoparasite cleaning service for other reef fishes. Cleaning stations are attended by many different species, congregating to wait their turn to be inspected and rid of any external parasites. Mexicans call this fish "El Barbero" ("the barber") because of this habit. These fish also feed on algae, molluscs, and crustaceans.
Distribution	Eastern Pacific region, from the Gulf of California to Panama. Also found at the Galapagos and other offshore islands.

Prognathodes aculeatus
Caribbean Longsnout Butterflyfish
(Poey 1860)

Kiyoshi Endoh

Habitat   Deep coral-rich reefs and drop-offs, between 1-90 m depth. Not common above 12 m.

Characters   Prolonged snout; pale to yellowish overall with dusky brown patch on rear upper body and dorsal fin (some variants may lack this patch); brown bar (sometimes faint) from forehead, through eye to snout; pelvic and anal fins yellowish. Reaches maximum size of 10 cm.

Remarks   A relatively secretive species which seeks refuge in crevices when approached. Generally solitary in occurrence, but sometimes paired. Feeds on small crustaceans, tubeworms, other invertebrates, and morsels of larger prey such as the tube feet of echinoderms. The most common butterflyfish in the Caribbean below 30 m depth. A recently discovered population living in cool waters off southern Brazil may represent a separate, undescribed species. It is characterized by a more vivid yellow coloration overall.

Distribution   Throughout the entire West Indies-Caribbean region to southern Florida, the western Gulf of Mexico and Venezuela.

224

Prognathodes aya
Doubleband Butterflyfish
Jordan 1866

Kiyoshi Endoh

Habitat	Deep offshore reefs, commonly between 20-170 m.
Characters	Silvery-white becoming yellowish dorsally with broad black band from middle of dorsal fin to base of anal fin; narrower black band from dorsal fin origin to just below eye. Maximum size about 15 cm. *Prognathodes guyanensis* (opposite) is similar but has an additional black band at rear upper corner of body. *Prognathodes marcellae* (page 230) from West Africa is also similar, but has more vibrant yellow coloration and a yellow margin on the gill cover.
Remarks	Originally described from a specimen taken from the stomach contents of a red snapper caught off the coast of Florida. The specific name is derived from that of the snapper: *Lutjanus aya*. Usually occurs below 45 m, consequently it is rarely seen by divers.
Distribution	Ranges along the continental shelf of the Gulf of Mexico and Florida Peninsula, northwards in the warm Gulf Stream to Cape Hatteras (North Carolina).

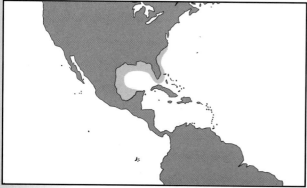

Prognathodes guyanensis
Threeband Butterflyfish
Durand 1960

Kiyoshi Endoh

Habitat Steep offshore rocky reefs, between 60-230 m, most abundant in excess of 100 m depth.

Characters Silvery-white becoming yellowish dorsally with two pale-edged black bands towards rear of body; third narrower black band passing from dorsal fin origin to just in front of eye. Attains 12.5 cm. *Prognathodes aya* (opposite) is similar in appearance, but has only two dark bands.

Remarks Seldom encountered by divers; usually seen only from deep-diving submersible craft. No information is presently available regarding the life history of this species.

Distribution Known from several localities in the West Indies including the Bahamas, Jamaica, Puerto Rico, Barbados, Belize and French Guinea.

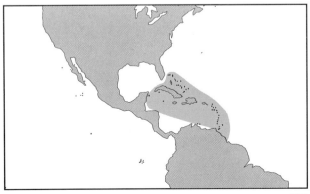

Prognathodes dichrous
Hedgehog Butterflyfish
Günther 1869

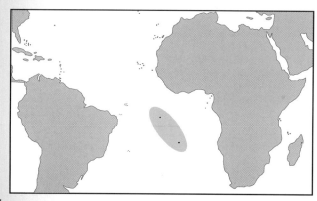

R. Lubbock/Ikan

Habitat Rocky areas, generally between 15-35 m but sometimes occurring shallower in caves or under ledges near the upper sections of drop-offs.

Characters Chocolate brown with conspicuous rectangular white patch on upper rear corner of the body and adjacent dorsal fin; caudal fin white; lateral line and eye silver. Attains 16 cm. *Prognathodes obliquus* (opposite) is almost identical in appearance, but has a triangular, rather than a rectangular-shaped white patch.

Remarks Occurs in pairs or small groups, commonly browsing over rocky bottoms in search of benthic invertebrates.

Distribution Occurs only at St. Helena and Ascension Island, isolated outposts in the central Atlantic Ocean.

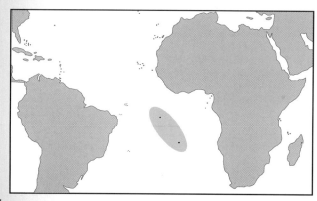

Prognathodes obliquus
Oblique Butterflyfish
Lubbock & Edwards 1980

R. Lubbock/Ikan

Habitat   Steep, rocky cliffs, usually below 55 m.

Characters   Chocolate brown overall with triangular white patch on upper rear corner of body and adjacent dorsal fin; caudal fin white; lateral line scales silver. Maximum size about 15 cm. *Prognathodes dichrous* (opposite) is very similar in appearance, but has a rectangular, rather than a triangular white patch on upper rear corner of body.

Remarks   Generally encountered in small aggregations containing up to about six individuals.

Distribution   Thus far known only from St. Paul's Rocks, on the mid-Atlantic Ridge just north of the equator.

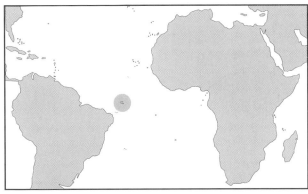

Prognathodes falcifer
Scythe Butterflyfish
Hubbs & Rechnitzer 1958

Roger Steene

Habitat   Deep rocky areas, usually between 30-150 m. Most common at about 100 m depth.

Characters   Creamy pale yellowish ground color with scythe-shaped black marking from gill cover to anal fin; black bar from anterior-most dorsal spines to eye; most of dorsal fin black; upper and lower edges of caudal fin black; pelvic fins yellow with black rear edge. Maximum size about 16 cm.

Remarks   Most common in depths not frequently visited by divers, but occurs in relatively shallow water (10-15 m) at the Galapagos Islands and Santa Catalina Island off California. Temperatures in these waters typically range between 16-20° C.

Distribution   Eastern Pacific Ocean, from southern California (Santa Catalina & La Jolla), northern Mexico (Guadelupe Island, Cabo San Lucas and West San Benito Island), and the Galapagos Islands.

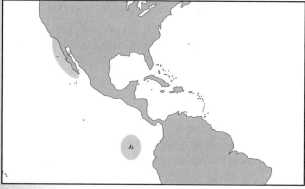

229

Prognathodes marcellae
Marcella Butterflyfish
Poll 1950

R. Lubbock/Ikan

Habitat   Deep rocky areas with isolated coral patches, from 15 to at least 95 m depth. Most common between 35-40 m. Prefers slopes adjacent to cool upwellings.

Characters   Silvery-white with a dark band along rear edge of body; another dark band from dorsal fin origin to eye; dark snout stripe; dorsal, anal and pelvic fins bright yellow; gill cover with bright yellow margin (lacking in the similar *Prognathodes aya*, page 225). Maximum size about 14 cm.

Remarks   Prefers steep slopes and is found singly, paired, or in small groups. Relatively easy to approach. The deep water habitat where this species abounds is seldom explored by divers. Water temperatures at these depths typically range between 16-19° C.

Distribution   Tropical west African coast from Senegal to the Congo River mouth. Also at the Cape Verde Islands, and probably other offshore islands in the Gulf of Guinea.

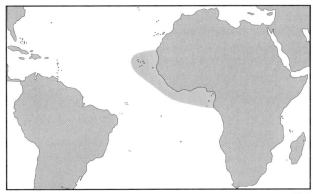

CHAPTER 5

ANGELFISHES & BUTTERFLYFISHES
IN THE AQUARIUM

Numerous volumes have been written covering all aspects of successful aquarium maintenance. In fact, the subject has virtually become a science of its own over the past few years. Therefore, it's beyond the scope of this book and totally unnecessary to devote detailed coverage of the subject. Moreover, angelfishes and butterflyfishes are not recommended for beginners. Those of you who keep them or intend doing so are most likely experienced hobbyists, well grounded in the basics. These fishes are not recommended for beginners simply because they are generally "touchy" with regards to handling, acclimation, and diet. It's best for newcomers to the marine hobby to make a gradual transition, first mastering the art of freshwater fish keeping, then graduating to the easier marine species such as damselfishes and wrasses. There is certainly no substitute for experience, but we can recommend three excellent references that contain a wealth of practical and theoretical information:

♦ **Dr. Burgess's Mini-Atlas of Marine Aquarium Fishes** by Warren E. Burgess, Herbert R. Axelrod, and Ray Hunziker (T.F.H. Publications, 1991).

♦ **Marine Aquarium Atlas** by Helmut Debelius and Hans A. Baensch (Mergus, 1994).

♦ **The Reef Aquarium** by J. Charles Delbeek and Julian Sprung (Ricordea Publishing, Volume 1-1994, Volume 2-1997).

We particularly recommend the last work, a very thorough compendium, which is widely acclaimed as the bible of marine-aquarium keeping.

A group of *Chaetodon melannotus* forages on a Red Sea reef. Hobbyists should strive to simulate natural conditions according to their chosen species. This includes clear water, optimal pH and electrolyte balance, and appropriate temperatures.

Although we will avoid a full blown discussion of basic aquarium keeping it is worthwhile to provide a few special tips that pertain to the art of successful angel and butterflyfish maintenance. Some of these may seem obvious, especially to our more experienced readers. We apologize for this, but many of you may not have kept these fishes previously, and they do require extra care compared to most species.

Be Prepared

The traditional Boy Scout motto is especially appropriate for these two families when it comes to introducing them to your home aquarium. Aquarium journalist Robert Fenner's analogy of butterflyfishes being like canaries in a coal mine is entirely appropriate. These delicate beauties are very susceptible to deteriorating water conditions and are the first fishes to show signs of distress if anything is amiss. Therefore it's essential to properly prepare for the arrival of your new fishes to insure they get off to a good start.

First we recommend isolating the new arrivals in a quarantine tank for 2-3 weeks. The fishes can be treated with a preventative antibiotic and/or copper solution at the same time just for insurance, although presumably the dealer has already attended to this chore. New fish should not be introduced to their permanent tank until they have fully settled in. This means the elimination of any signs of distress, abnormal behavior, or disease accompanied by an eagerness to feed.

The intended permanent tank should contain compatible fishes, but this is always an unpredictable factor and may require removal of any "bullies" that continuously intimidate the new arrivals. When first introduced, angelfishes and butterflyfishes are often timid and make easy targets for aggressive fish. For this reason ample rock shelter in the form of crevices and caves need to be provided. This will simulate their natural habitat, which invariably contains an abundance of hiding places. We do not recommend keeping these fishes with soft and hard corals, anemones or small invertebrates. They will most likely end up eating them or at least inflicting damage. However, advanced hobbyists can no doubt formulate viable fish-invertebrate communities that will allow their coexistence.

The bigger the better when it comes to choosing the correct aquarium size. Adults are accustomed to wide open spaces in nature and a large tank size will promote growth of juveniles. As a rough guideline allow 100 liters (26 gallons) of water for each 10 cm (4 inches) of fish length, although this figure is variable depending on the filtration/water movement system. The fishes should never be introduced to freshly set up tanks. Rather the aquarium should be aged for at least 4-6 weeks to insure the buildup of special bacteria that help breakdown harmful nitrogen compounds that are produced once fish are introduced. Alternatively, water can be siphoned from an established tank and diluted with 20-30 percent "new" water that has aged for at least one week.

Selection and Handling

Don't say we didn't warn you, but many butterflyfish are not suitable for captivity, mainly due to problems associated with diet (see below). Angelfishes may also prove stubborn customers, particularly the specialized algal feeders. No other family is so variable as butterflyfishes as far as their adaptability to captive conditions is concerned. Many are well suited and make excellent pets, but many others have a dismal track record and are a waste of time, not to mention money. The natural feeding regime is probably the best single guide for deciding which species have the best chance of survival in captivity. This information is lacking for most of the rare and deep-water species, but they are probably best avoided anyway. We urge our readers to stick with the tried and true species marked with the appropriate symbol in the species accounts appearing in Chapters 3 and 4.

This symbol, which appears with the species accounts in Chapters 3 and 4, indicates the suitability of a particular species for captivity. Three-star fishes are the easiest to care for, one and two-star species are recommended for advanced hobbyists. A question mark (?) is used for species that are very uncommon in the aquarium hobby, indicating that their suitability for captivity is unknown.

The best species for captivity are usually those which are omnivores, accustomed to feeding on a wide variety of items. The diet of a typical omnivore (e.g. *Chaetodon auriga*, page 97) usually contains green algae, sessile invertebrates such as corals, sponges, barnacles and tunicates, and mobile benthic invertebrates including various worms, prawns, and crabs. Plankton feeders are also good candidates, as evidenced by the success rates of species such as *Heniochus diphreutes* (page 190) and *Hemitaurichthys polylepis* (page 187). Beware of specialized coral feeders, especially those entirely dependent on this food source. Because they are totally obliged to feed on corals they are sometimes referred to as *obligates*. Coral obligates include some of the most beautiful members of the butterflyfish family, but don't be tempted. Many of the species will flat-out refuse to feed, no matter what's offered. Although it may be possible to keep some of the obligates alive by providing chunks of live coral to the tank at regular intervals, this chore usually exceeds the bounds of time and effort most hobbyists have at their disposal, not to mention access to an unlimited supply of the proper sorts of coral.

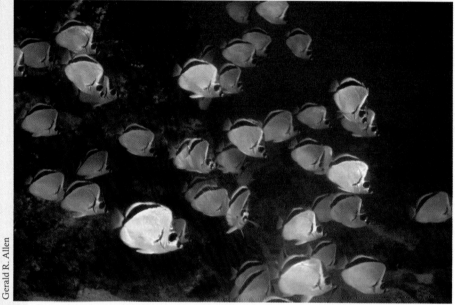

Gerald R. Allen

A feeding shoal of *Johnrandallia nigrirostris* at the Galapagos Islands. Plankton feeding species such as this usually adapt well to aquarium conditions.

Only by refusing to purchase the incompatible species will we eventually discourage their unnecessary and wasteful collection. It's a sad testament to the hobby that these "living dead" are regularly offered for sale by retailers. This is certainly an appropriate term as they begin an ordeal of death by starvation the moment they are captured.

On a brighter note, there are many excellent choices available - fishes that adapt well to aquarium conditions and provide their owners with many months or even years of enjoyment. But certain precautions must be taken when selecting the prospective fishes from your local dealer. Members of both families are highly susceptible to collecting, handling and shipping induced stress. Therefore, care must be exercised to insure only the healthiest fish are purchased. First and foremost, always observe the prospective fish carefully to make sure it is in good physical shape without any obvious sign of disease or handling damage (i.e. abrasions, torn fins, missing scales). Ask the dealer to offer some food. It's a very good sign if the fish feeds enthusiastically and has a good physical appearance, including a vivid color pattern. Also ask the dealer what quarantine procedure the fish has been subjected to, including the use of preventive antibiotics, copper treatment, or freshwater dips. All of these are recommended treatments for new butterflyfish and angelfish arrivals. In fact, you may wish to repeat them during the home quarantine period, just to be on the safe side.

Avoid selection of very small fish (less than about 5 cm or 2 inches) or large fish (greater than 15 cm or 6 inches) as they have the least chance of successfully adapting to aquarium conditions. Also, don't be tempted to purchase pairs, trios, or small groups of the same species. They seldom get along with one another in captivity. It's better to select individuals belonging to different species if several fishes are purchased.

Having made the selection it's important to get the fish home as quickly as possible and settled into its new surroundings. If lengthy transport time involving several hours is unavoidable insist on an extra large bag that is well oxygenated. Once home, the bag should first be floated in the quarantine tank to equalize the temperature, then the bag is gradually diluted with water from the same tank. This procedure will avoid the shock of sudden changes of temperature and pH, which are potentially lethal. After a 50 percent gradual dilution (over a period of about 30 minutes) the fish and water in the bag can be poured into the quarantine tank. This method eliminates direct handling and risk of injury to the fish. Any contaminants in the bag water can be dealt with during the quarantine period, which should last for 2-3 weeks. Low illumination in the quarantine tank is advisable and should be left on for the first few nights until the fish is used to its new surroundings.

Subtle reminders

We promised not to discuss basics, but a few subtle reminders are in order at this point. We only mention these because all are important aspects of successful angelfish and butterflyfish keeping. Refer to any of the three references we cited at the beginning of the chapter for further details.

Temperature - All but a few species are tropical, which means an optimal temperature range between 24-28°C (75-82°F) A variety of efficient thermostatically controlled submersible heaters are available from pet dealers. Make sure the one you select delivers sufficient wattage to heat the amount of water in your tank. Another popular option is to heat the entire aquarium room rather than individual tanks.

pH and salinity - These parameters need to be carefully monitored with appropriate testing equipment. The natural salinity should be maintained, which ranges between 31 and 34 parts per thousand. Red Sea species are most at home at the higher end of the scale. Salinity can be measured with a hydrometer, which gives a reading of specific gravity. Readings between 1.023 and 1.025 are satisfactory. The pH should be maintained between 8.2-8.3. Use of calcium carbonate substrates (coral rubble, dolomite) will help to maintain an acceptable value.

Lighting - Either florescent tubes or metal halide lamps are recommended. Metal halide lamps are far more expensive and really not necessary for success. This type of lighting is most suitable for reef community tanks featuring corals and algae. Since corals and butterflyfishes are incompatible there's no need for strong illumination. Florescent tubes are perfectly adequate for fish. One tube for every 10 cm (4 inches) of aquarium width is recommended. These tubes can be combined with actinic bulbs for special lighting effects. The soft actinic lighting can be left on in the evening or throughout the night without disturbing the fishes normal rest pattern.

Filtration - Nitrogen buildup in the form of ammonia and nitrite, is the biggest worry confronting marine aquarists. It's impossible to avoid these toxic compounds when keeping fishes, but there are many tried and true filtration methods for getting rid of them. These include various internal and external systems from simple sub-gravel biological filters to sophisticated multichambered affairs which occupy considerable space outside the main aquarium. The important thing is too choose a system that effectively eliminates the nasty nitrogen compounds. There are many good systems on the market. Seek the advice of an experienced aquarist or your dealer. We personally prefer Marineland's Emperor. This compact and silent external unit provides six separate sites for mechanical, chemical, and biological filtration. The model that fits our larger tanks filters more than 1,500 liters (400 gallons) of water per hour, providing good oxygenation and water movement, important features in simulating the natural environment of these fishes.

Skimmers - A protein skimmer is highly recommended, particularly for tanks larger than 380 liters (100 gallons). It's a vital safeguard for the removal of unwanted nitrogen compounds and other pollutants and can be effectively combined with any filtration system. Another name for this device is a foam fractionator. It's basically the same process used by sewage-treatment plants. A fine stream of bubbles is directed through a large tube. Any contaminants present attach themselves to the bubbles and are conveyed upwards where they collect as foam in an easily-cleaned chamber. One advantage of this method over standard filtration is that nitrogen-containing substances are instantly removed, without having to be oxidized biologically.

Air supply - A reliable air supply has many uses. It can be utilized with skimmers or to provide additional water movement in large tanks. It's also handy for cultivating brine shrimp. If you maintain freshwater fishes in nearby aquaria extra air stones are always beneficial. For years the first author (GRA) struggled with various small pumps sold by pet shops. Regardless of size or price they had one common characteristic, all were unreliable and malfunctioned sooner or later. Vibrator pumps with replaceable diaphragms are the worst. Not only are they unreliable, but noisy as well. I battled on with these for years until an aquarium friend introduced me to a heavy duty industrial type pump. Although it is expensive (about $500) the money is well spent, especially if you have a number of aquariums and a desire for totally dependable, unlimited air. My Sakuragawa Hiblow model 40GJ-L pump is a very compact and streamlined unit that delivers 40 cubic liters of air per minute, far more than needed to aerate 20 tanks, including several in excess of 380 liters (100 gallons). What's more the unit is silent and virtually maintenance free.

Feeding - Variety is the key to success. Remember that most of the highly recommended species have omnivorous diets and naturally feed on a wide range of items. An excellent range of dry, frozen, and live foods are available from reputable pet dealers. Do not offer a static diet, but constantly introduce new items and keep rotating old ones. Flake foods should be offered in small amounts to make sure its eaten and does not foul the tank. A quantity that is consumed over a 2-3 minute period is satisfactory. Several small feedings per day is much better than one or two large ones. This generalization pertains to all types of foods. Remember, in nature these fishes feed all day long. Acceptable frozen foods include adult brine shrimp, daphnia, shrimp, crab, fish, mussels, oysters, beef heart, steak, chicken, and various commercial marine "mixes". Most standard live fare, including freshwater organisms (mosquito larvae, daphnia, etc.), are acceptable. A steady supply of live brine shrimp is recommended for plankton feeders such as *Genicanthus* and *Hemitaurichthys*. Various worms are also good, including chopped earthworms, tubifex worms, and whiteworms. Don't be afraid to experiment with live foods, but always with very small quantities at first. Plant matter is important for most omnivores and absolutely essential for all angelfishes. Commercial flakes or pellets and frozen preparations often contain vegetables. The inventive hobbyists can manufacture various mixes, blending finely chopped green leafy vegetables (e.g. spinach) with sea food or other meats. Most *Centropyge* thrive on a diet that contains at least 50 percent vegetable matter. Marine algae is particularly good and can either be grown in the aquarium or obtained from oriental food stores in the form of dried seaweed. Angelfishes will also eat steamed or microwaved zucchini rind, romaine lettuce, spinach, and peas. Hobbyists living near the sea can offer occasional treats in the form of "live rocks". Some pet dealers sell frozen angelfish mix that has a significant vegetable content as well as sponge material.

Diseases - Angelfishes and butterflyfishes are susceptible to the usual aquarium maladies, all the more so if water quality deteriorates. Some of the more common infectious ailments include white spot, velvet, gill fluke, *Oodinium*, ich, and fungus. If caught in time all of these can be cured with standard remedies such as copper sulfate and malachite green. Remember, these are infectious diseases so the whole aquarium must be treated for complete eradication. Filtration equipment needs to be switched off when medication is added and additional aeration should be introduced.

Breeding - Breeding butterfly and angelfishes remains only a dream for the average home aquarist. These fishes are very sensitive to environmental disturbance and its impossible to simulate the natural habitat in the average home to the extent necessary to promote breeding. Indeed, it's a major challenge for public aquaria and research institutions. Even under more or less ideal conditions only a few species have spawned in captivity. Even fewer have been successfully reared. The usual scenario is that the very frail larvae perish after the first 2-3 days.

Tank mates - These fishes are often found in pairs or groups in nature, but members of the same species usually fight amongst themselves in captivity. This tendency is especially pronounced among the species of *Pomacanthus* and *Holacanthus,* and many of the butterflyfishes. Mixed species are usually compatible, but to be on the safe side it's best to keep species together that are not closely related. Most butterfly and angelfishes are suitable for community tanks, but fish size needs to be carefully considered. Larger individuals are less likely to be picked on in a tank containing mainly adult fishes.

Gerald R. Allen

Shoal of *Holacanthus clarionensis* at Clarion Island, E. Pacific Ocean. Captive angelfishes require substantial amounts of algae in their diet.

How Long Do Angelfishes and Butterflyfishes Live?

This question has long bewildered scientists and lay persons alike. There is a general scarcity of accurate information regarding the life spans of members of both these families. However, thanks to Professor Bruno Condé and the staff of the Tropical Aquarium of the Museum of Zoology in Nancy, France we now have a much better understanding of this aspect of the life history. Condé and his staff are renowned for their fine marine displays and ability to maintain captive fishes for exceptionally long periods. They attribute their success to providing plenty of space, good water quality, and catering to individual dietary requirements. Their success is all the more remarkable considering that Nancy is situated well inland, hundreds of kilometers from the sea. Over the years Professor Condé has kept meticulous longevity records. The figures obtained for angelfishes and butterflyfishes are particularly remarkable - their life span is much longer than most scientists previously suspected. The record for an angelfish is 26 years for *Pomacanthus navarchus* and *P. xanthometopon* and 25 years for *Chaetodon ephippium*. All of these individuals are still going strong. Recent unpublished studies involving age determination by reading otolith (ear bone) growth rings indicate similar longevity in nature. Professor Condé has kindly provided the table which appears below. We don't expect the average home aquarist to duplicate these impressive figures, but there is ample evidence your aquarium pets will provide years of enjoyment if properly cared for.

Longevity record for Angelfishes and Butterflyfishes
still alive at the Nancy Aquarium (July 1997)

Angelfishes		Butterflyfishes	
Pomacanthus navarchus	26 yrs	*Chaetodon ephippium*	25 yrs
Pomacanthus xanthometopon	26 yrs	*Heniochus varius*	20 yrs
Pomacanthus sexstriatus	25 yrs, 7 mths	*Chaetodon ulietensis*	19 yrs
Apolemichthys trimaculatus	24 yrs	*Heniochus acuminatus*	19 yrs
Apolemichthys xanthurus	23 yrs, 10 mths	*Forcipiger flavissimus*	18 yrs
Pomacanthus maculosus	22 yrs	*Hemitaurichthys zoster*	17 yrs
Centropyge tibicen	21 yrs	*Heniochus intermedius*	17 yrs
Paracentropyge multifasciata	19 yrs	*Chaetodon rafflesi*	16 yrs
Pomacanthus asfur	17 yrs	*Forcipiger longirostris*	16 yrs
Genicanthus bellus	17 yrs	*Hemitaurichthys polylepis*	15 yrs
Chaetodontoplus duboulayi	17 yrs	*Heniochus chrysostomus*	15 yrs
Pygoplites diacanthus	16 yrs, 8 mths	*Chaetodon plebius*	13 yrs
Pomacanthus imperator	15 yrs	*Chaetodon auriga*	12 yrs
Chaetodontoplus mesoleucus	12 yrs	*Chaetodon mitratus*	12 yrs
Chaetodontoplus meredithi	11 yrs	*Chelmon rostratus*	10 yrs
Holacanthus bermudensis	11 yrs		
Genicanthus watanabei	11 yrs		
Desmoholacanthus arcuatus	10 yrs		

The ultimate aquarium

The end of this chapter and book seems an appropriate place to relate a memorable experience with keeping these marvelous fishes. If it sparks a bit of envy don't feel too bad - it was a rare and unusual situation, which is not likely to happen again. Even though it happened to me (GRA) there is a sharp twinge of longing for the good old days every time I think about it. The story goes back to 1971, when I worked as a marine biologist for the Marine Resources Department on the Micronesian island of Palau. My wife Connie and son Tony found ourselves in an enviable position. The house we were assigned to live in was built on stilts above a coral reef overlooking a picturesque lagoon. We enjoyed catching breakfast every morning with rod and reel from our verandah. In the evenings a light suspended below the house attracted a wealth of interesting creatures including a type of cardinalfish (*Sphaeramia orbicularis*), which made a perfect subject for a fascinating life history study I eventually published. The story gets even better.

During a brief shopping trip to the island of Guam, the nearest civilization, I bought a 20 gallon plastic aquarium complete with lighting hood, pump, and subgravel filter. We installed the tank in a corner of the living room and for the next few months, until we eventually left the island, it provided us with more enjoyment than any aquarium we've ever owned. It was exclusively inhabited by angelfishes and butterflyfishes, usually only 1-3 species at a time. But now comes the good part. Although the small tank was a closed system I made daily water changes, exchanging about half the water. This was easy, just a matter of scooping out the water, tossing it over the balcony and lowering a bucket tied to a rope for a refill.

Stocking the tank with corals and fishes was great fun. I usually went out with six year-old Tony for a couple of hours every Saturday morning. I would swim from the house and cover several hundred meters, towing Tony who held a collecting bucket while lying on an air mattress. The water was shallow, beautifully warm, and crystal clear with an abundance of coral and fishes. There was a wide range of angels and butterflies to choose from, about 15 species just off the back doorstep! I collected only juveniles, which could be comfortably accommodated in the small tank. Some of our favorites included *Centropyge bicolor, Chaetodon auriga, C. ephippium, C. lunula, C. melannotus, C. ornatissimus, C. octofasciatus, C. rafflesi, C. trifascialis, C. lunulatus,* and *C. vagabundus.* You probably noticed some of the species are among those not recommended for captivity, but I was not bound by the normal guidelines. A fresh crop of new corals were gathered every week, which satisfied the requirements of the specialist feeders. We never kept any fish or corals for more than a week or two. It was far more fun to dump them back onto the reef from the verandah and simply go out and catch replacements. Understandably, marine aquarium keeping has never been quite the same.

Palau's famous rock islands are home to many butterfly and angelfish species.

Roger Steene

237

Genus *Apolemichthys*   Fraser-Brunner, 1933

Characters: Similar to *Holacanthus*, but preorbital convex without strong spines; also interoperculum without strong spines and preopercular spine not deeply grooved; scales on cheek small and irregular.

Species: *A. arcuatus, A.griffisi, A. guezei, A. kingi, A. trimaculatus, A. xanthopunctatus, A. xanthotis, A. xanthurus.*

Genus *Centropyge*   Kaup, 1860

Characters: Scales relatively large; interoperculum, small and serrated or with posterior spines; lateral line terminating at end of soft dorsal; hind margin of preorbital free.

Subgenus *Centropyge*   Kaup, 1860

Characters: Gill rakers 14-19; post-temporal bone with spinules; scales rounded, their width and length about equal; lower edge of opercular bone straight.

Species: *C. aurantia, C. bicolor, C. colini, C. eibli, C. flavissima, C. heraldi, C. multispinis, C. narcosis, C. nox, C. tibicen, C. vroliki.*

Subgenus *Xiphypops*   Jordan and Jordan, 1922

Characters: Gill rakers 20-25; post-temporal bone without spinules; scales squarish, their width greater than length; lower edge of opercular bone convex.

Species: *Centropyge acanthops, C. argi, C. aurantonota, C. bispinosa, C. debelius, C. ferrugata, C. fisheri, C. flavicauda, C. flavipectoralis, C. hotumatua, C. interrupta, C. joculator, C. loricula, C. milticolor, C. nahackyi, C. nigriocella, C. potteri, C. resplendens, C. shepardi.*

Genus *Chaetodontoplus*   Bleeker, 1876

Characters: Scales very small (86 or more in lateral row) and not arranged in regular series; hind margin of preorbital not free; interoperculum large without spines; lateral line terminating at end of soft dorsal; vertical fins not elongate.

Species: *C. ballinae, C. caeruleopunctatus, C. chrysocephalus, C. conspicillatus, C. duboulayi, C. melanosoma, C. meridithi, C. mesoleucus, C. niger, C. personifer, C. septentrionalis.*

Genus *Genicanthus*   Swainson, 1839

Characters: Scales relatively large in regular series; lateral line terminating at end of soft dorsal; interoperculum large; teeth in jaws relatively short, their length contained about five times in eye diameter; scales on operculum in 6-8 rows; caudal fin emarginate to strongly lunate.

Species: *G. bellus, G. caudovittatus, G. larmarck, G. melanospilos, G. personatus, G. semicinctus, G. semifasciatus, G. spinus, G. watanabei, Genicanthus n. sp.*

Genus *Holacanthus*   Lacepède 1803

Characters: Scales relatively large in regular series; lateral line terminating at end of soft dorsal; interoperculum large; teeth in jaws relatively long, their length contained less than 2-3 times in eye diameter; scales on operculum in about 9 rows; caudal fin truncate.

Subgenus *Angelichthys*   Jordan and Evermann, 1896

Characters: Preorbital without strong spines, a few small ones sometimes present; stout spines on rear edge of preoperculum; lateral line interrupted, a short separate portion on base of caudal fin; scales on head moderately spiny; dorsal and anal fins forming filaments in adults; Atlantic distribution.

Species: *H. africanus, H. bermudensis, H. ciliaris.*

Subgenus *Holacanthus*   Lacepède, 1803

Characters: Preorbital bone angular with strong spines; interoperculum with strong spines anteriorly; preopercular spine deeply grooved; scales on cheek moderate-sized, in about 8-10 rows; dorsal and anal fins forming filaments in adults; smaller auxillary scale at base of each body scale; Atlantic distribution.

Species: *H. tricolor.*

Subgenus *Plitops*   Fraser-Brunner, 1933

Characters: Preorbital bone angular with strong spines; interoperculum with strong spines anteriorly; preopercular spine deeply grooved; scales on cheek small, in irregular rows; each scale on body with several small auxillary scales; lateral line obscure, terminating below end of soft dorsal fin; Eastern Pacific distribution.

Species: *H. clarionensis, H. limbaughi, H. passer.*

Genus *Paracentropyge*   Burgess, 1803

Characters: Head and body with pattern of about nine alternating dark and light bars; body relatively deep, the depth 1.5-1.7 in standard length; gill rakers 14-18; dorsal fin rays XIII or XIV, 17-19; tips of pelvic fins filamentous.

Species: *P. boylei, P. multifasciata, P. venusta.*

Genus *Pomacanthus*   Lacepède, 1803

Characters: Scales either relatively large or small; scale focus exposed to cteni area; lateral line complete; hind margin of preorbital not free; interoperculum large, without spines; color pattern often undergoes dramatic transformation from juvenile to adult stage; vertical fins or pelvic fins usually elongate.

Subgenus *Euxiphipops*   Fraser-Bruner, 1934

Characters: Scales rhombic, relatively large, about 50 in lateral line; no auxillary scales present on body; lower margin of preorbital bone convex; preoperculum with a few strong spines on lower limb; interoperculum relatively large without spines; lateral line complete; 12-14 dorsal spines; pelvic fins long and filamentous; caudal fin rounded; dorsal and anal fin with rounded profile.

Species: *P. navarchus, P. sexstriatus, P. xanthometopon.*

Subgenus *Pomacanthodes*   Gill, 1862

Characters: Soft anal fin not produced into a filament; body moderately compressed; 11 to 14 dorsal spines; juveniles with more than 4 transverse bars between eye and base of caudal fin.

Species: *P. annularis, P. asfur, P. chrysurus, P. imperator, P. maculosus, P. semicirculatus, P. striatus, P. zonipectus.*

Subgenus *Pomacanthus*   Lacepède, 1803

Characters: Soft anal fin produced into a filament; body strongly compressed; 9 or 10 dorsal spines; juveniles with 4 transverse bars between eye and base of caudal fin.

Species: *P. arcuatus, P. paru.*

Genus *Pygoplites*   Fraser-Brunner, 1933

Characters: Scales relatively large in regular series; lateral line terminating at end of soft dorsal; interoperculum without spines, posteriorly with a narrow branch reaching the suboperculum; preorbital convex, without spines, its hind margin not free and not serrated; scales on operculum in about 8 rows.

Species: *P. diacanthus.*

APPENDIX II   GENERA AND SUBGENERA OF BUTTERFLYFISHES

Genus *Amphichaetodon*   Burgess, 1978

Characters: Dorsal spines 12; dorsal fin triangular; lateral line complete with 47-55 scales; snout moderate, 2.4-3.3 times in length of head; lacrymal bone scaled.
Species: *A. howensis, A. melbae.*

Genus *Chaetodon*   Linnaeus, 1758

Characters: Dorsal spines 11-16; dorsal fin variably shaped; lateral line incomplete with 22-55 scales; snout variable, 1.9-4.5 in length of head; scalation of lacrymal bone variable.
Species: see subgenera below.

Subgenus *Chaetodon*   Linnaeus, 1758
Characters: Dorsal rays XI-XIV,18-25; anal rays III,16-19; rear edge of dorsal and anal fins with blunt angles; snout short, pointed, 2,7-3.3 in length of head; lacrymal bone free and smooth; lateral line in a high arc; scales variably shaped, rounded to angular.
Species: *C. assarius, C. blackburnii, C. capistratus, C. citrinellus, C. daedalma, C. dialeucos, C. dolosus, C. fremblii, C. guentheri, C. guttatissimus, C. hoefleri, C. humeralis, C. kleinii, C. litus, C. marleyi, C. melannotus, C. miliaris, C. multicinctus, C. ocellatus, C. ocellicaudus, C. pelewensis, C. punctatofasciatus, C. quadrimaculatus, C. robustus, C. sanctaehelenae, C. sedentarius, C. smithi, C. striatus, C. trichrous.*

Subgenus *Chaetodontops*   Bleeker, 1876
Characters: Dorsal rays XII,23-26; anal rays III,17-22; rear edge of dorsal and anal fins with blunt angles; snout short, 2.8-3.5 in length of head; lateral line in a high, angular arc; lacrymal free and rounded; teeth normal; scales rounded.
Species: *C. adiergastos, C. auripes, C. collare, C. fasciatus, C. flavirostris, C. lunula, C. reticulatus, C. semilarvatus, C. wiebeli.*

Subgenus *Citharoedus*   Kaup, 1860
Characters: Dorsal rays XII,23-28; anal rays III,19-23; spinous dorsal fin evenly graduated, soft portion of dorsal and anal with blunt angle posteriorly; snout short, 3.0-4.0 in length of head; lateral line arc high and angular; teeth in undefined rows at front of jaws; supraorbital horns present in *tholichthys* larval stage.
Species: *C. meyeri, C. ornatissimus.*

Subgenus *Corralochaetodon*   Burgess, 1978
Characters: Dorsal rays XIII,20-21; anal rays III,19; spinous dorsal fin evenly graduated, soft portion of dorsal and anal with rounded angle posteriorly; snout short, 3.1-4-1 in length of head; lateral line in a high, angular arc; teeth grouped in undefined rows at front of jaws; lacrymal almost completely hidden by scales; scales vertically elongate.
Species: *C. austriacus, C. lunulatus, C. melapterus, C. trifasciatus.*

Subgenus *Discochaetodon*   Nalbant, 1971
Characters: Dorsal rays XI,19-22; anal rays III,16-18; dorsal and anal fins strongly rounded; snout short, 2.8-4.5 in length of head; lateral line in a low, smooth arc; lacrymal restricted; scales rounded.
Species: *C. aureofasciatus, C. octofasciatus, C. rainfordi, C. tricinctus.*

Subgenus *Gonochaetodon*   Bleeker, 1876
Characters: Dorsal rays XI,24-25; anal rays III,20-22; dorsal fin elevated, spines increasing in length posteriorly; lateral line in a moderately smooth arc; lacrymal free and smooth; scales rhomboid, arranged in a chevron pattern.
Species: *C. baronessa, C. larvatus, C. triangulum*

Subgenus *Lepidochaetodon*   Bleeker, 1876
Characters: Dorsal rays XIII,21-22; anal rays III,19; dorsal and anal fins rounded; snout short, 2.5-3.2 in length of head; lateral line in a high, smooth arc; lacrymal partly hidden; teeth in regular rows, the outermost strongest.
Species: *C. unimaculatus.*

Subgenus *Megaprotodon*   Guichenot, 1848
Characters: Dorsal rays XIV,15; anal rays IV,15; spinous dorsal fin rounded, spines increasing in length to 5th spine; soft portion of dorsal and anal fins pointed; lateral line in a low arc; scales rhomboid, arranged in a chevron pattern.
Species: *C. trifascialis.*

Subgenus *Radophorus*   Swainson, 1839
Characters: Dorsal rays XII-XIV,20-25; anal rays III,19-22; dorsal and anal fins with blunt angle posteriorly; snout pointed, slightly projecting, 1.9-2.8 in head length; lateral line a high, angular arc; lacrymal free and smooth; scales angular.
Species: *C. auriga, C. decussatus, C. ephippium, C. falcula, C. gardineri, C. leucoplerua, C. lineolatus, C. mesoleucos, C. nigropunctatus, C. oxycephalus, C. rafflesi, C. selene, C. semeion, C. ulietensis, C. vagabundus, C. xanthocephalus.*

Subgenus *Rhombochaetodon*   Burgess, 1978
Characters: Dorsal rays XIII,20-23; anal rays III,16-17; spinous dorsal rounded to nearly triangular; soft dorsal fin rounded posteriorly, anal fin angular; snout pointed, 2.6-3.2 in length of head; lateral line in a low arc; scales rhomboid, arranged in a chevron pattern.
Species: *C. argentatus, C. mertensii, C. paucifasciatus, C. xanthurus.*

Subgenus *Roa*   Jordan, 1923
Characters: Dorsal rays XIII,19-22; anal rays III,16; spinous dorsal with triangular shape, 3rd or 4th spine the longest; 2nd anal spine significantly longer than 3rd; rear edge of dorsal and anal fins approximately vertical; snout pointed, 2.7-3.7 in length of head; ocular band vertical below eye; scaly sheath of dorsal fin low.
Species: *C. burgessi, C. declivis, C. excelsa, C. flavocoronatus, C. mitratus, C. modestus, C. nippon, C. tinkeri.*

Subgenus *Tetrachaetodon*   Weber and de Beaufort, 1936
Characters: Dorsal rays XIV,16-17; anal rays III-IV,15-16; dorsal spines graduated; dorsal and anal fins rounded posteriorly; snout blunt and short, 3.0-4.0 in length of head; lateral line in a low arc; lacrymal partly hidden by scales; base of spinous dorsal fin about twice length of soft dorsal base; scales rounded.
Species: *C. bennetti, C. plebeius, C. speculum, C. zanzibariensis.*

Genus *Chelmon*   Cloquet, 1817

Characters: Dorsal spines 9; dorsal fin spines increasing in length posteriorly; lateral line complete with 45-55 scales; snout elongate, 1.7-3.0 in length of head; no scales on lacrymal bone.
Species: *C. marginalis, C. muelleri, C. rostratus.*

Genus *Clelmonops*   Bleeker, 1876

Characters: Dorsal spines 11; dorsal fin spines increasing in length posteriorly; lateral line complete with 51-56 scales; snout elongate, 2.2-2.6 in length of head; no scales on lacrymal bone.
Species: *C. curiosus, C. truncatus.*

Genus *Coradion*   Kaup, 1860

Characters: Dorsal spines 8-10; dorsal fin spines increasing in length posteriorly; lateral line complete with 43-52 scales; snout short, 2.9-3.8 in length of head; lacrymal bone scaled.
Species: *C. altivelis, C. chrysozonus, C. melanopus.*

Genus *Forcipiger*   Jordan and McGregor, 1898

Characters: Dorsal spines 11 or 12; spinous dorsal deeply incised between spines; lateral line complete with 66-80 scales; snout elongate, 1.4-2.1 in length of head; lacrymal bone partly scaled.
Species: *F. flavissimus, F. longirostris.*

Genus *Hemitaurichthys*   Bleeker, 1876

Characters: Dorsal spines 12-16; dorsal fin rounded in shape; lateral line complete with 70-90 scales; snout short, 2.5-3.6 in length of head; lacrymal bone partly scaled.

Species: *H. multispinosus, H. polylepis, H. thompsoni, H. zoster.*

Genus *Heniochus*   Cuvier, 1817

Characters: Dorsal spines 11 or 12; dorsal spine elongate; lateral line complete with 40-60 scales; snout moderate, 2.5-4.5 in head length; lacrymal bone partly scaled.

Species: *H. acuminatus, H. chrysostomus, H. diphreutes, H. intermedius, H. monoceros, H. pleurotaenia, H. singularius, H. varius.*

Genus *Johnrandallia*   Nalbant, 1974

Characters: Dorsal spines 12; 4th dorsal spine the longest, remaining spines decreasing in length; lateral line complete with 52-63 scales; snout short, 3.0-3.5 in length of head; no scales on lacrymal bone.

Species: *J. nigrirostris.*

Genus *Parachaetodon*   Bleeker, 1874

Characters: Dorsal spines 6; dorsal spines increasing in length posteriorly; lateral line incomplete with 40-43 scales; snout short, 2.8-3.8 in length of head; lacrymal bone scaled.

Species: *P. ocellatus.*

Genus *Prognathodes*   Gill, 1862

Characters: Dorsal spines 13; spinous dorsal with triangular shape, 3rd or 4th spine the longest; 2nd anal spine significantly longer than 3rd; dorsal fin notched, with rear edge of dorsal and anal fins approximately vertical; snout projecting, 2.1-2.9 in length of head; eye band absent or angled anteriorly below eye; scaly sheath at base of dorsal fin low.

Species: *P. aculeatus, P. aya, P. dichrous, P. falcifer, P. guezei, P. guyanensis, P. guyotensis, P. marcellae.*

REFERENCES & RECOMMENDED READING

Allen, G.R. 1980. *Butterfly and Angelfishes of the World*. John Wiley & Sons, New York. **2**: 149-352 (also German, French, and Swedish language eds.).

Bouchon-Navaro, Y. 1980. Quantitative distribution of the Chaetodontidae on a fringing reef of the Jordanian coast (Gulf of Aqaba, Red Sea). *Tethys* 9(3): 247-251.

Bouchon-Navaro, Y. 1981. Quantitative distribution of the Chaetodontidae on a reef of Moorea Island (French Polynesia). *J. exp. Mar. Biol. Ecol.* **55**: 145-157.

Burgess, W.E. 1974. Evidence for the elevation to family status of the angelfishes (Pomacanthidae), previously considered to be a subfamily of the butterflyfish family, Chaetodontidae. *Pac. Sci.* **28**(1): 57-71.

Burgess, W.E. 1978. *A monograph of the butterflyfishes (Family Chaetodontidae)*. T.F.H. Publications, Inc., Neptune New Jersey.

Ehrlich. P.R., Talbot, F.H., Russell, B.C. & Anderson, G.R.V. 1977. The behaviour of chaetodontid fishes with special reference to Lorenz's "poster colouration" hypothesis. *J. zool., Lond.* **183**: 213-228.

Feddern. H.A. 1968. Hybridization between the western Atlantic angelfishes, *Holacanthus isabelita* and *H. ciliaris*. *Bull. Mar. Sci.* **18**(2): 351-382.

Fraser-Brunner, A. 1933. A revision of the chaetodont fishes of the subfamily Pomacanthinae. *Proc. Zool. Soc. London,* **1933**: 543-599.

Hamilton, W.J. III & Petermann, R.M. 1971. Countershading in the colorful reef fish *Chaetodon lunula*: concealment, communication, or both? *Anim. Beh.* **19**(2): 357-364.

Hioki, S. & Suzuki, K. 1995. Spawning behavior, eggs, larvae, and hermaphroditism of the angelfish, *Apolemichthys trimaculatus,* in captivity. *Bull. Inst. Oceanic Res. & Develop., Tokai Univ.* **16**: 13-22.

Hioki, S., Suzuki, K. & Tanaka, Y. 1990. Development of eggs and larvae in the angelfish, *Centropyge ferrugatus*. *Japan. J. Ichthyol.* 37(1): 34-38.

Hubbs, C.L. 1963. *Chaetodon aya* and related deep-living butterflyfishes: their variation, distribution, and synonymy. *Bull. Mar. Sci.* **13**(1): 133-192.

Kishimoto, H., Hioki, S. & Suzuki, K. 1996. Transfer of *Centropyge multispinis* (Teleostei, Pomacanthidae) from subgenus *Xiphypops* to subgenus *Centropyge*. *Ichthyol. Res.* **43**(2): 153-159.

Krupp, F. and Debelius, H. 1990. The hybrid of *Centropyge multifasciatus* x *Holacanthus venustus* from the Philippines and notes on aberrant colour forms of *Centropyge multispinis* from the Maldives and the Red Sea. *Revue fr. Aquariol.* **17**(1990) 2: 53-56.

Leis, J.M. 1989. Larval biology of butterflyfishes (Pisces, Chaetodontidae): what do we really know? *Environ. Biol.* **25**(1-3): 87-100.

Lobel, P.S. 1978. Diel, lunar, and seasonal periodicity in the reproductive behavior of the pomacanthid fish, *Centropyge potteri,* and some other reef fishes in Hawaii. *Pac. Sci.* **32**(2): 193-207.

Lobel, P.S. 1989. Spawning behavior of *Chaetodon multicinctus* (Chaetodontidae); pairs and intruders. *Environmental Biology of Fishes.* **25**(1-3): 125-130.

Mok, H-K. & Shen, S-C. 1982. Phylogeny of the chaetodontids on the basis of kidney and intestinal differences. *Japan. J. Ichthyol.* **29**(1): 43-61.

Moyer, J.T. 1981. Interspecific spawning of the Pygmy Angelfishes *Centropyge shepardi* and *Centropyge bispinosus* at Guam. *Micronesica* **17**(1-2): 119-124.

Moyer, J.T. & Nakazono, A. 1978. Population structure, reproductive behavior, and protogynous hermaphroditism in the angelfish *Centropyge interruptus* at Miyake-jima, Japan. *Japan. J. Ichthyol.* **25**(1): 25-39.

Nalbant, T. 1973. Studies on chaetodont fishes with some remarks on their taxonomy (Pisces, Perciformes, Chaetodontidae). *Travaux Mus. Hist. Nat. "Grigore Antipa"* **13**: 303-331.

Nalbant, T. 1974. Some osteological characters in butterfly fishes with special references to their phylogeny and evolution (Pisces, Perciformes, Chaetodontidae). *Travaux Mus. Hist. Nat. "Grigore Antipa"* **15**: 303-314.

Neudecker, S. & Lobel, P.S. 1982. Mating systems of chaetodontid and pomacanthid fishes at St. Croix. *Z. Tierpsychol.* **59**: 299-318.

Ogilby, J.D. 1915. Review of the Queensland Pomacanthinae. *Mem. Qld. Mus.* **3**: 99-116.

Okuno, R. 1962. Intra- and interspecific relations of salt-water fishes in aquarium. 1. Butterflyfishes. *Japan. J. Ecol.* **12**(4): 129-133.

Pyle, R.L. & Randall, J.E. 1994. A review of hybridization in marine angelfishes (Perciformes: Pomacanthidae). *Environmental Biology of Fishes.* **41**: 127-145.

Ralston, S. 1976. Anomalous growth and reproductive patterns in populations of *Chaetodon miliaris* (Pisces, Chaetodontidae) from Kanehoe Bay, Oahu, Hawaiian Islands. *Pac. Sci.* **30**(4): 395-403.

Randall, J.E. 1975. A revision of the Indo-Pacific angelfish genus *Genicanthus*, with descriptions of three new species. *Bull. Mar. Sci.* **25**(3): 393-421.

Randall, J.E., Allen, G.R. & Steene, R.C. 1977. Five probable hybrid butterflyfishes of the genus *Chaetodon* from the central and western Pacific. *Rec. West. Aust. Mus.* **6**(1): 3-26.

Reese, E.S. 1973. Duration of residence by coral reef fishes on "home" reefs. *Copeia*, No. 1: 145-149.

Reese, E.S. 1975. A comparative field study of the social behaviour and related ecology of reef fishes of the family Chaetodontidae. *Z. Tierpsychol.* **37**: 37-61.

Reese, E.S. 1977. Coevolution of corals and coral feeding fishes of the family Chaetodontidae. *Proc. Third Int. Coral Reef Symp.* **1**: 267-274.

Sano, M. 1989. Feeding habits of Japanese butterflyfishes (Chaetodontidae). *Environmental Biology of Fishes.* **25**(1-3): 195-203.

Shen, S.C. 1973. Ecological and morphological study on fish-fauna from the waters around Taiwan and its adjacent islands. 3. Study on the chaetodont fishes (Chaetodontidae) with description of a new species and its distribution. *Rept. Inst. Fish. Biol. Nat. Taiwan Univ.* **3**(1): 1-75.

Shen, S.C. & Liu, C.H. 1976. Ecological and morphological study of the fish fauna from the waters around Taiwan and its adjacent islands. 17 - A study of sex reversal in a pomacanthid fish *Genicanthus semifasciatus* (Kamohara). *Acta Oceanographica Taiwanica Sci. Reports Nat. Taiwan Univ.* No. 6: 140-150.

Shen, S.C. & Liu, C.H. 1979. Clarification of the genera of the angelfishes (family Pomacanthidae). *Acta Oceanographica Taiwanica Sci. Reports Nat. Taiwan Univ.*: 57-77.

Smith, J.L.B. 1949. The fishes of the family Pomacanthidae in the Western Indian Ocean. *Ann. Mag. nat. Hist.* 12 **8**: 377-384.

Snow, J.L. & Rylander, M.K. 1982. A quantitative study of the optic system of butterflyfishes (family Chaetodontidae). *J. Hirnforsch.* **23**: 121-125.

Steene, R.C. 1978. *Butterfly and Angelfishes of the world.* A.H. & A.W. Reed Pty. Ltd., Wellington. **1**: 1-144.

Suzuki, K., Hioki, S., Tanaka, Y. & Iwasa, K. 1979. Spawning behavior, eggs, larvae, and sex reversal of two Pomacanthine fishes, *Genicanthus lamarck* and *G. semifasciatus,* in the aquarium. *J. mar. Sci. Technol., Tokai Univ.* **12**: 149-165.

Suzuki, K., Tanaka, Y. & Hioki, S. 1980. Spawning behavior, eggs, and larvae of the butterflyfish, *Chaetodon nippon,* in an aquarium. *Japan. J. Ichthyol.* **26**(4): 334-341.

Thresher, R.E. 1982. Courtship and spawning in the Emperor Angelfish *Pomacanthus imperator,* with comments on reproduction by other pomacanthid fishes. *Mar. Biol.* **70**: 149-156.

Thresher, R.E. & Brothers, E.B. 1985. Reproductive ecology and biogeography of Indo-West Pacific angelfishes (Pisces: Pomacanthidae). *Evolution* **39**(4): 878-887.

Yabuta, S. 1997. Spawning migrations in the monogamous butterflyfish, *Chaetodon trifasciatus.* *Ichthyol. Res.* **44**(2): 177-182.

Yabuta, S. & Kawashima, M. 1997. Spawning behavior and haremic mating system in the corallivorous butterflyfish, *Chaetodon trifascialis,* at Kuroshima Island, Okinawa. *Ichthyol. Res.* **44**(2): 183-188.

Yasuda, F. 1967. Some observations on the color of the young forms of *Chaetodontoplus septentrionalis* (T. & S.). *Sci. Rep. Yokosuka City Mus.* **13**: 78-81.

Yasuda, F. & Zama, A. 1975. Notes on the two rare chaetodont fishes, *Parachaetodon ocellatus* and *Coradion chrysozonus* from the Ogasawara Islands. *J. Tokyo Univ. Fish.* **61**(1): 33-38.

Zumpe, D. 1964. Laboratory observations on the aggressive behaviour of some butterfly fishes (Chaetodontidae). *Z. Tierpsychol.* **22**(2): 226-236.

GLOSSARY

Anterior: the front (-most) section(s).
Benthic: associated with the bottom of the ocean.
Dorsal: the upper part of the body of a fish.
Demarcated: distinctly separated.
Endemic: occuring only in one localised area or region (species).
Conspecific: a member of the same species.
Ventral: the lower part of the body of a fish.
Ovate: shaped like an egg.
Truncate: squared off, with a flat edge at the end (eg. tail).
Ground Color (Ground): the major constituent color comprising the overall appearance of the fish.
Home-ranging: tending to stay in the same general territory throughout life (species).
Ocellus: a marking that mimics the appearance of an eye (pl. **ocelli**).
Ecto-parasites: small invertebrates that attach to the external parts of a larger host animal on whose tissue it sustains itself.
Substrate: the bottom; may be rocky, sandy, coral covered, etc.
Posterior: the rear (-most) section(s).
Pelagic: pertaining to the open ocean away from coastal waters.
Protractile: capable of being protruded.
Speciation: an evolutionary process whereby several distinct and advanced species descend from a common more primitive ancestral parent species.
Gravid: pregnant female ladened with unreleased eggs.
Median Fins: the dorsal, caudal and anal fins.
Sympatric: overlapping distributions (populations, species).
Gametes: mature reproductive cells; eggs in females, sperm in males.
Type Species: the first species of a particular genus to be scientifically described and named.

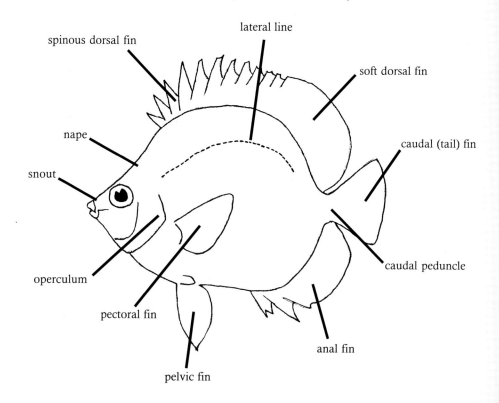

INDEX

Several discoveries of rare and new species have surfaced just prior to the publication of this book. Fortunately there was still time to at least give them limited coverage on this page. We thank the following persons who provided photographs: 1) Phil Woodhead; 2) Tomonori Hiata; 3) Richard Pyle; 4)Julian Sprung.

1) *Centropyge* sp. - Woodhead's Pygmy Angel: A close relative of *C. heraldi* (p. 46), this species is known only from rubble bottoms (depth range 9-20 m) in the Coral Sea off Australia's Great Barrier Reef. It is easily distinguished by its overall yellow coloration and the oblong dark blotch on the posterior portion of the dorsal fin. The species will soon be described by Rudie Kuiter of Melbourne, Australia.

2) *Chaetodontoplus niger* - Black Angelfish: This species is treated in the main text and illustrated with a painting (see p. 64). Living specimens were photgraphed for the first time at Wakayama and Kochi prefectures, southern Honshu (Japan), at depths between 20-80 m. This photgraph illustrates a juvenile (3.5 cm TL), which differs slightly from the adult in possessing a black bar on the outer margin of the tail.

3) *Prognathodes* sp. 1 - Orange-margin Butterflyfish: Richard Pyle (see pp. 4-5) recently collected seven specimens of this beautiful fish at the islands of Hawaii and Oahu using his special deep-diving SCUBA equipment. This new species is relatively common but confined to depths (115-120 m) well below those usually penetrated by divers. Specimens are on display at the Waikiki Aquarium.

4) *Prognathodes* sp. 2 - Brazilian Butteflfyish: Closely related to *P. aculeatus* (p. 224), but apparently an undescribed species that is confined to cool temperate waters of southern Brazil.